The Best Of Alex 2007

Charles Peattie & Russell Taylor

Masterley Publishing

The Best Of
Alex
2007

First published in 2007 by MASTERLEY PUBLISHING

Layout and Artwork: Suzette Field & Maurice Citron

ISBN: 978-1-85375-631-3

Our usual thanks go to our sponsors:
FTSE Group - provider of global equity, fixed income, alternative asset class, responsible investment & investment strategy indices; and Mondo Visione - publisher of 'The Handbook of World Stock, Derivative and Commodity Exchanges'. Not only have they lent their generous support to this annual but also to the West End stage adaptation of Alex.

So may we encourage you to make use of the valuable services they offer (but, please, not during the performance..)

FOREWORD

Who would believe it? Alex is twenty years old. Yet it seems only yesterday that he took proud possession of his first mobile phone.

To be honest, when we were given the chance back in 1987 to create a cartoon strip satirising a social phenomenon known as Yuppies (remember them?) it seemed like a handy gig that might pay the rent for six months or so. This shocking new breed wore expensive suits, drove BMWs, talked openly about their salaries (yes, yes, all that was shocking back then) and carried these new-fangled gadgets that we'd never actually seen and no one had even decided on a name for but which were generally referred to as "portable telephones". Such accessories were proper status symbols in that they were huge and people could see that you had one even from several hundred yards off.

These vulgar contraptions that everyone (well, everyone who didn't have one) grumbled about quickly became a central theme of the strip. In fact one of our earliest jokes was Alex in a box at the theatre ringing Clive's phone to embarrass him about sitting in the cheap seats. Who'd have thought that we'd end up making what we must now modestly describe as a career out of writing two decades' worth of gags about telephones?

Of course mobile phones have evolved into BlackBerries these days and much technology has been and gone over Alex's lifetime. He used to be proud of owning a fax machine (how embarrassing.. when was the last time you saw one of those?). When he started just to possess a computer was a status symbol - even if you didn't know how to switch it on - and there were no such things as email or the internet (how on earth did people pass the time in the office? They must have had to actually do some work.)

And now, on the occasion of his vicennial, Alex is to be seen in the theatre again, but this time starring in his own West End show. So, if you haven't already done so, book some tickets, charge them to your corporate credit card, and come and help us celebrate our creation's unexpected longevity. But regrettably – and this may seem the height of ingratitude – we will have to ask you to switch off your mobiles.

Charles Peattie Russell Taylor

Charles Peattie and Russell Taylor

Alex
Devious investment banker

Penny
Alex's under-appreciated wife

Clive
Alex's ineffectual colleague

Christopher
Alex's teenage son

Rupert
Very senior banker

Bridget
Clive's scary wife

Carolyn
Alex's client (and mistress)

Cyrus
Alex's workaholic American boss

Christian
Annoying Eurotrash junior

Alex
PEATTIE+TAYLOR
SO THE BANK HAS OUTSOURCED YET ANOTHER AREA OF ITS OPERATIONS TO BANGALORE?
YES.
alex@alexcartoon.com

QUITE A LOT OF OUR CLERICAL AND BACK OFFICE FUNCTIONS ARE NOW HANDLED OUT THERE... IT COSTS A TINY FRACTION OF THE SALARIES WE'D HAVE TO PAY TO GET THE JOB DONE OVER HERE...

£5,000 PER YEAR IS A GOOD WAGE FOR THEM. IT MEANS OUR WORKERS THERE ARE WELL INCENTIVISED TO BE DILIGENT IN PERFORMING THIS LATEST ROLE...

SUBJECTING EXPENSES CLAIMS TO AN EXACTING PROCESS OF VERIFICATION?
YES. IT REALLY HACKS THEM OFF WHEN A BROKER SPENDS THE EQUIVALENT OF 3 MONTHS OF THEIR PAY ON DINNER WITH A CLIENT...
PLEASE FORWARD ALL THE SUPPORTING BILLS AND RECEIPTS...
SIGH

Alex
PEATTIE+TAYLOR
IT MUST HAVE FELT STRANGE YOUR SON DOING WORK EXPERIENCE IN THE CITY, ALEX...
YES, IT DID...
alex@alexcartoon.com

I SUPPOSE THERE'S A SENSE IN WHICH PARENTS DON'T WANT THEIR CHILDREN EVER TO GROW UP, BUT INSTEAD TO KEEP THEM ETERNALLY COCOONED OFF FROM THE REALITIES OF THE ADULT WORLD...

BUT THERE COMES A TIME WHEN ONE HAS TO LET GO... AND ONCE THE CHILD HAS LOST ITS INNOCENCE - AS IT WERE - THINGS CAN NEVER REALLY BE THE SAME AGAIN...

THE SACRIFICES I'VE HAD TO MAKE TO PAY FOR YOUR EDUCATION, CHRISTOPHER...
SACRIFICES...?! YEAH-RIGHT! I'VE SEEN THEM: LONG LUNCHES... GOLF DAYS... WATCHING CRICKET ON THE OFFICE TV...

Alex
PEATTIE+TAYLOR
ALEX, I CAN'T BELIEVE YOU'VE TAKEN YOUR WIFE TO THE HOTEL WHERE WE ALWAYS STAY IN NEW YORK.
YUH. I KNOW, CAROLYN...
alex@alexcartoon.com

THE THING IS: THIS IS A VERY FAMOUS ESTABLISHMENT... SHE'S ALWAYS WANTED TO COME HERE... IF I'D REFUSED SHE MIGHT HAVE GUESSED I'M HAVING AN AFFAIR...

TO THINK THAT IMPECCABLE STANDARD OF PERSONAL SERVICE IS BEING WASTED ON HER... I HOPE SHE AT LEAST APPRECIATES IT...
WELL, I'M NOT SURE SHE DOES...

HELLO, MR SMITH... NICE TO SEE YOU AGAIN, SIR...
I THOUGHT ALL THE STAFF HERE WERE DRILLED TO REMEMBER GUESTS' NAMES.
ER... YES... MOST SLACK OF HIM...

Alex
PEATTIE+TAYLOR
OF COURSE AMERICAN BANKERS LIKE CYRUS HAVE THEIR LIFESTYLES OVER HERE FUNDED BY GENEROUS RELOCATION PACKAGES...

RENT ON THE TROPHY HOUSE IN CHELSEA, FEES FOR THE KIDS AT THE BEST PRIVATE SCHOOLS, DOMESTIC STAFF... ALL PAID FOR BY THE BANK...
alex@alexcartoon.com

HOW'S IT SUPPOSED TO MAKE THE REST OF US FEEL, TO SEE OUR EMPLOYER UNQUESTIONINGLY SIGN OFF EVERY HUGE BILL CYRUS SUBMITS FOR EXPENDITURE ON HIS PERSONAL LIFE?

SUCH AS THE ONE FROM HIS GENTLEMAN'S OUTFITTERS FOR HIS SHOOTING KIT?
I DID WARN HIM TO GO TO A 2ND HAND SHOP... HEE HEE...
I SAY: - TWEEDS THAT MATCH?!
CLEARLY BRAND NEW... TSK TSK...

Alex
PEATTIE + TAYLOR
I DON'T GET IT... THESE GUYS HAVE PAID THOUSANDS TO COME ON THIS SHOOT BUT THEY LOOK LIKE A BUNCH OF HOBOS...
IT'S ALL PART OF CLASSIC BRITISH UNDER-STATEMENT, CYRUS...
YOU GOTTA DRESS FOR SUCCESS, ALEX. WHAT'S THE POINT IN LOOKING LIKE A LOSER..?
LET ME TELL YOU: IN THIS LIFE MONEY ACCRUES TO PEOPLE LIKE ME WHO PRESENT A SMART, WELL TURNED OUT, TAILORED PROFESSIONAL IMAGE...
WELL YES BUT...
CYRUS IS NOT PLEASED ABOUT YOU TIPPING HIM AFTER THE SHOOT, SIR ADRIAN.
I AM SO SORRY... IT WAS THOSE NEW TWEEDS... I ASSUMED HE MUST'VE BEEN GIVEN THEM BY OUR HOST TO BREAK THEM IN FOR HIM... AND THAT HE WAS THE GAMEKEEPER...
alex@alexcartoon.com

Alex
PEATTIE + TAYLOR
OBVIOUSLY I FELT ANGRY WITH JUSTIN HAWKINS WHEN HE RESIGNED FROM US TO GO WORK FOR A COMPETITOR LAST WEEK...
BUT YOU MUST NEVER LET THESE FEELINGS INTRUDE OUTSIDE WORK. HIS WIFE AND MINE HAVE ALWAYS GOT ON, SO I WAS VERY COURTEOUS WHEN WE BUMPED INTO THEM IN A RESTAURANT LAST NIGHT...
THAT'S WHEN HIS WIFE MENTIONED TO YOURS THAT JUSTIN WOULD BE USING HIS 3 MONTHS' GARDEN-ING LEAVE TO TAKE HER AND THE KIDS ON A ROUND THE WORLD TRIP?
YES.
SO I PHONED HIS NEW BOSS THIS MORNING AND SAID I WAS RELEASING JUSTIN FROM HIS CONTRACT WITH US AND HE WAS FREE TO START WORK THERE IMMEDIATELY...
EXCELLENT. SCUPPERED HIS PLANS THEN.
alex@alexcartoon.com

Alex
PEATTIE + TAYLOR
SO I HEAR YOU'RE TAKING A TWO-WEEK VACATION, CYRUS...
I BET YOU'LL BE GLAD TO SEE ME GONE, ALEX...
NOT HAVING ME AROUND TO CHECK UP ON YOU, HUH?
ACTUALLY I'M AWAY MYSELF FROM NEXT WEEK, SO YOUR CYNICISM IS MISPLACED...
I JUST THINK IT'S A NICE THING THAT A GUY WHO DRIVES HIMSELF AS HARD AS YOU DO SHOULD FINALLY BE TREATING HIMSELF TO A BIT OF TIME OFF...
THANKS, ALEX. I APPRECIATE THE SENTIMENTS...
SO YOUR THEORY IS THAT HE'S BEEN HEADHUNTED TO A NEW JOB AND IS USING UP HIS HOLIDAY ALLOWANCE?
PLEASE GOD LET'S HOPE SO...
alex@alexcartoon.com

Alex
PEATTIE + TAYLOR
OVER THE SUMMER WE'VE ALLOWED STAFF TO REMOVE THEIR TIES IN THE OFFICE... SHOULD WE NOW RESCIND THIS POLICY?
WELL, I THINK ONE'S GOT TO TAKE INTO CONSIDERATION THE TRADITIONAL INVERSE CORRELATION BETWEEN THE PROFITABILITY OF THE FINANCIAL SECTOR AND THE DRESS CODES IT IMPOSES...
BASICALLY WE DRESS DOWN IN UPTURNS AND UP IN DOWNTURNS...
TRUE, AND THE BANK'S HAD A GOOD YEAR... SO OUR DECISION IS CLEAR...
GET THEM ALL BACK IN THEIR TIES IMMEDIATELY...
QUITE. THE BONUS SEASON'S NOW ON US AND EXPECTATIONS ARE ALREADY DANGEROUSLY OUT OF HAND.
alex@alexcartoon.com

Alex
PEATTIE + TAYLOR
ONE TENDS TO ASSUME THAT, BEING AMERICAN, CYRUS IS IN LEAGUE WITH THE FORCES OF DARKNESS THAT BLIGHT OUR LIVES...
WHAT...? COMPLIANCE?
alex@alexcartoon.com

EXACTLY, BUT ONE SHOULDN'T FORGET THAT HE FINDS THEIR CONSTANT INTERFERING JUST AS FRUSTRATING AS WE DO...

AND, LIKE US, HE SPENDS A GOOD PROPORTION OF HIS TIME GRUMBLING ABOUT HOW THEY PREVENT HIM FROM DOING HIS JOB...

LITERALLY, IN HIS CASE...
I WAS FORCED TO TAKE TWO CONSECUTIVE WEEKS OF VACATION... YES: VACATION... GODDAM COMPLIANCE RULES...
TANNED GLOW
TRAGIC, ISN'T IT?

Alex
PEATTIE + TAYLOR
IT'S SUCH A SHAME THAT THE STRIKE I ORGANISED ACHIEVED NOTHING IN THE END...
YES, I AGREE.
CITY PRICES
alex@alexcartoon.com

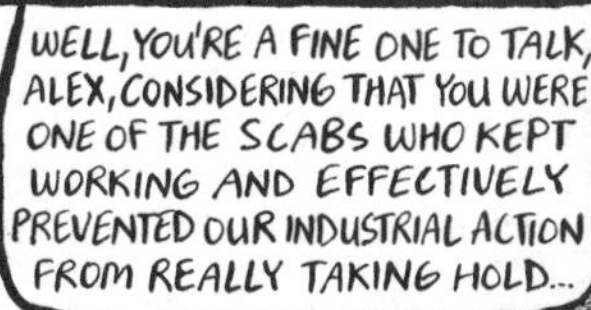

WELL, YOU'RE A FINE ONE TO TALK, ALEX, CONSIDERING THAT YOU WERE ONE OF THE SCABS WHO KEPT WORKING AND EFFECTIVELY PREVENTED OUR INDUSTRIAL ACTION FROM REALLY TAKING HOLD...

I STILL FANTASISE ABOUT THE EFFECT IT WOULD HAVE HAD ON A BIG ORGANISATION LIKE MEGABANK IF THE MOOD OF DISSENT HAD SPREAD AND WE'D BEEN JOINED IN OUR STRIKE BY DEPARTMENT AFTER DEPARTMENT...
YES...

COMPLIANCE, H.R., CORPORATE COMMS, DIVERSITY... JUST THINK HOW MUCH THE REST OF US COULD HAVE GOT DONE WITH NONE OF THEM AROUND... SIGH

Alex
PEATTIE + TAYLOR
I'M PUTTING TOGETHER THE GRAPHICS FOR A PRESENTATION ON THE BANK'S DRIVE TOWARDS BECOMING "CARBON NEUTRAL".
alex@alexcartoon.com

THE SEMINAR, WHICH WILL BE COMPULSORY FOR ALL STAFF, HAS BEEN ORGANISED TO WARN OF THE DANGERS OF CO_2 AND GLOBAL WARMING CAUSED BY GREENHOUSE GASES

SEE... THE CHEMICAL SYMBOLS REPRESENTING ONE ATOM OF CARBON AND 2 OF OXYGEN WHIRL AROUND AND THEN COME TOGETHER TO SPELL OUT THE IDENTITY OF THE MAIN CULPRIT...

OOPS... I HAVEN'T QUITE GOT IT RIGHT YET...
AH YES... "CHIEF OPERATING OFFICER"... THE POMPOUS LITTLE TWERP: DREAMING UP ALL THIS TWADDLE TO WASTE OUR TIME...
COO

Alex
PEATTIE + TAYLOR
SONYA, I'VE JUST REALISED THIS FINANCIAL P.R. PARTY IS TONIGHT... YOU DID ACCEPT ON MY BEHALF?
YES, OF COURSE.
INVITE
alex@alexcartoon.com

AH, GOOD, THANKS...
BUT, ALEX, YOU'RE ALWAYS VERY SNOOTY ABOUT THESE P.R. DOS AND GO ON ABOUT HOW DULL THEY ARE.

WHATEVER I MAY FEEL ABOUT SUCH EVENTS SOCIALLY, CLIVE, I WOULD NEVER SPURN THE OPPORTUNITY THEY PRESENT TO MAINTAIN ONE'S PROFILE IN THE BUSINESS WORLD...

LOOK THERE'S A BADGE FOR ALEX MASTERLEY...
HE HASN'T SHOWN UP. NO DOUBT BUSY ON SOME BIG DEAL...
RECEPTION

Alex
PEATTIE + TAYLOR
SO, YOU BUSY AT THE MOMENT, STEVE?
BUSY'S NOT THE WORD, CLIVE...

AS YOU'RE AWARE, THE BANK'S MOVING OFFICES IN A FEW WEEKS WHICH MEANS THAT MY ROLE AS HEAD OF PREMISES HAS SUDDENLY BECOME CRUCIAL...

YOU CAN IMAGINE THE SORT OF LOAD THAT'S BEEN PLACED ON ME... IT'S GOING TO BE ABSOLUTELY HECTIC FROM NOW TILL THE DAY OF THE MOVE...

ER, SO NO CHANCE OF MY BUYING YOU LUNCH TO DISCUSS MY OFFICE REQUIREMENTS...
FORGET IT... I'M BOOKED SOLID...
AH, STEVE... I'VE GOT A CAB WAITING TO TAKE US TO THE RESTAURANT...
SLIDE

Alex
PEATTIE + TAYLOR
OBVIOUSLY AS THE BANK'S HEAD OF PREMISES I'M IN CHARGE OF THE MOVE TO THE NEW BUILDING...

BUT OF COURSE THE COMPLIANCE DEPARTMENT WILL BE HEAVILY INVOLVED... THEY'RE PLANNING TO USE THE OPPORTUNITY TO ERRECT FURTHER CHINESE WALLS...
PREDICTABLY...

HAVING SAID THAT, ONE HAS TO ACCEPT THAT THERE'S A NEED FOR THESE PHYSICAL BARRIERS ON DEALING FLOORS TO PREVENT THE WRONG PEOPLE GETTING ACCESS TO PRIVILEGED INFORMATION...

FOR EXAMPLE YOUR BOSS SEEING WHAT YOU'RE ACTUALLY LOOKING AT ON YOUR SCREEN?
QUITE... SO MAKE SURE I SIT WITH MY BACK TO ONE OF THE WALLS PLEASE...

Alex
PEATTIE + TAYLOR
SO, AS HEAD OF PREMISES YOU'RE ORGANISING THE BIG OFFICE MOVE NEXT MONTH, STEVE?
THAT'S RIGHT, ALEX.

FRANKLY IT'S A LOGISTICAL NIGHT-MARE, ATTEMPTING TO RELOCATE ALL OUR STAFF INTO A NEW BUILDING PLUS TRYING TO ACCOMMODATE EVERYONE'S INDIVIDUAL NEEDS...

OBVIOUSLY I'M WORKING IN CLOSE CONJUNCTION WITH THE VARIOUS HEADS OF DEPARTMENT WHOSE JOB IT IS TO MAKE ALL THE TOUGH DECISIONS REQUIRED...

CYRUS, DO YOU WANT TO KEEP FIVE OF YOUR TEAM OR HAVE AN EXTRA 20 SQUARE FEET ON YOUR NEW OFFICE?
WELL, IT HAS TO BE THE OFFICE...
OKAY, I'LL TELL H.R. TO HAVE THE P45s READY...

Alex
PEATTIE + TAYLOR
I'VE GOT A PHD IN NUCLEAR PHYSICS. I NEVER IMAGINED I'D END UP WORKING IN A BANK...
I THOUGHT I'D BE DISCOVERING NEW SUBATOMIC PARTICLES OR POSTULATING THEORIES ABOUT THE ORIGINS OF THE UNIVERSE...
YOU MAY NOT BE SERVING HUMANITY AT LARGE BUT YOU'RE INVALUABLE TO US...

HAVING QUANTS LIKE YOU WITH THE MATHEMATICAL SKILLS TO CONSTRUCT COMPLEX ALGORITHMS CAPABLE OF HANDLING MULTIPLE PARAMETERS AND VARIABLES IS VITAL TO THE BANK...
YES, BUT DOING THE SEATING PLAN FOR THE NEW OFFICE MOVE?
HERE'S A FULL LIST OF ALL THE PEOPLE WHO REFUSE TO SIT NEXT TO EACH OTHER... AND ALL THOSE WHO ARE DEMANDING CORNER OFFICES...

Alex
PEATTIE + TAYLOR
I SEE THIS NEW EUROPEAN DIRECTIVE ON AGEISM COMES INTO FORCE NEXT MONTH...
YES...
alex@alexcartoon.com

FROM THEN ON IT WILL BECOME ILLEGAL TO FIRE PEOPLE ON GROUNDS OF AGE... SO IF THE BANK WANTS TO GET RID OF US OLD TIMERS IT'LL HAVE TO ACT QUICKLY...

YOU KNOW, PEOPLE LIKE ME HAVE GIVEN LONG YEARS OF SERVICE TO THIS ORGANISATION AND WHAT ARE WE GIVEN IN RETURN FOR OUR LOYALTY?

ER... LOADS AND LOADS OF SHARE OPTIONS?
EXACTLY... AND THE ONLY WAY TO CASH THEM ALL IN IS TO GET MADE REDUNDANT... SO IT'S NOW OR NEVER FOR ME...
CROSS

Alex
PEATTIE + TAYLOR
OH NO! ... MY HUSBAND...
WHAT THE HELL'S GOING ON BETWEEN YOU AND MY WIFE?
alex@alexcartoon.com

YOU WANT TO MAKE SOMETHING OF IT?
YES I DO... COME ON: PUT 'EM UP IF YOU'RE ANY SORT OF A MAN, ALEX...
HOLD ON!

LOOK AT YOU TWO. YOU'RE BOTH PROFESSIONAL PEOPLE AND YOU WANT TO TRADE PUNCHES IN A PUBLIC PLACE? WHAT ARE YOU THINKING OF...? WHAT POSSIBLE GOOD WILL THIS DO?

NICE IDEA OF YOURS, CAROLYN... AT LEAST THIS WAY IT DOES SOME GOOD...
QUITE. £50 TO CHARITY TO SEE THESE TWO WIMPS SLUG IT OUT. WELL WORTH IT...
WHITE COLLAR BOXING

Alex
PEATTIE + TAYLOR
OH NO... I SHOULD NEVER HAVE ALLOWED ALEX TO FIGHT MY HUSBAND IN THIS WHITE-COLLAR BOXING BOUT...
alex@alexcartoon.com

ALEX IS AN INVESTMENT BANKER FOR GOODNESS' SAKE... HOW CAN HE BE EXPECTED TO SURVIVE HALF AN HOUR IN A BOXING RING?

I CAN'T BEAR TO SEE HIM TAKING THIS SORT OF PUNISHMENT... THIS IS INHUMAN... STOP IT IMMEDIATELY!
BUT, CAROLYN, IT'S THE BREAK BETWEEN ROUNDS...

EXACTLY... AND JUST LOOK AT HIM TRYING TO OPERATE HIS BLACKBERRY WEARING BOXING GLOVES...
FRUSTRATION
FUMBLE
IT'S TRAGIC I AGREE...

Alex
PEATTIE + TAYLOR
WOW... IS THAT ALEX MASTERLEY IN THE RING?! WHO'S HE FIGHTING...?
WHITE COLLAR BOXING
alex@alexcartoon.com

THE HUSBAND OF ONE OF HIS CLIENTS. A CHAP CALLED HOWARD... I CAN'T REMEMBER WHAT HE DOES FOR A LIVING...
OH MY GOD... DID YOU SEE THAT...?

ALEX HAS FELLED HIM WITH A LEFT HOOK... HE'S ON THE CANVAS.. HE'S TRYING TO GET UP BUT HE'S LOOKING GROGGY... THE REF'S CHECKING IF HE'S OKAY TO GO ON...

HOW MANY FINGERS?
ER... HOW MANY DO YOU WANT THERE TO BE?
AH YES... I REMEMBER NOW: HE'S A MANAGEMENT CONSULTANT...

Alex
PEATTIE + TAYLOR
OH NO... ALEX HAS LET HIS GUARD DOWN AND HE'S BEEN FELLED BY A RIGHT HOOK...

alex@alexcartoon.com
HE'S FLAT OUT ON THE CANVAS... THERE'S NO WAY HE'S GOING TO GET UP IN TIME...
ONE... TWO... THREE...

BUT, HOLD ON... HE'S ROUSING HIMSELF... HE'S GROGGY, BLEARY, DISORIENTATED BUT INSTINCTIVELY HE'S DRAGGING HIMSELF TO HIS FEET... WHERE DOES A BANKER GET THAT SORT OF SHEER WILLPOWER?
FOUR.... FIVE.... SIX...
BEEP BEEP

FROM ALL THOSE FIVE A.M. STARTS AFTER LATE NIGHT BOOZING SESSIONS WITH THE MONEYBROKERS...
THANKS, CLIVE...
BEEP BEEP

Alex
PEATTIE + TAYLOR
YOU CAN'T GO ON, ALEX. YOU'VE GOT A BLACK EYE AND A BADLY CUT LIP...
WHITE COLLAR BOXING

alex@alexcartoon.com
I'M GOING TO HAVE TO THROW IN THE TOWEL
NO, CLIVE... I REFUSE TO LET YOU DO THAT...

CAN'T YOU SEE I'M FIGHTING HERE FOR MY HONOUR AND DIGNITY IN FRONT OF HUNDREDS OF PEOPLE, MANY OF WHOM ARE MY PEERS IN THE FINANCIAL WORLD...

HERE... WE'LL THROW IN THIS ONE INSTEAD... I STOLE IT FROM THAT SEVEN STAR HOTEL IN DUBAI...

Alex
PEATTIE + TAYLOR
WITH THE BANK MOVING OFFICES IN A FEW WEEKS ALMOST NO WORK IS GETTING DONE ROUND HERE...

EVERYONE IS SUDDENLY TOTALLY FIXATED ON GETTING THEMSELVES THE BEST OFFICE IN THE NEW BUILDING, THE LATEST STATE-OF-THE-ART CHAIR, THE MOST UP-TO-DATE COMPUTER...

alex@alexcartoon.com

IN FACT CERTAIN PEOPLE SEEM TO BE DEVELOPING AN EXAGGERATED SENSE OF THEIR OWN IMPORTANCE AND GETTING HIGHLY PERNICKETY ABOUT WHAT THEY EXPECT TO BE GIVEN...

WHAT'S THIS? A CASE OF NON VINTAGE CHAMPAGNE FROM CLIVE? WHO DOES HE THINK I AM, BRIBING ME WITH RUBBISH LIKE THIS?
HEAD OF PREMISES
12 BOTTLES

Alex
PEATTIE + TAYLOR
AN OFFICE MOVE IS A CHANCE FOR DEPARTMENTS TO SHOW HOW HIGHLY THEY RANK IN THE CORPORATE PECKING ORDER...

alex@alexcartoon.com
EVERYONE WANTS TO GET THE BEST FLOOR IN THE NEW BUILDING. EITHER THE FIRST FLOOR FOR EASY ACCESS OR THE TOP FLOOR FOR THE SUPERIOR VIEWS...

SO OBVIOUSLY AS HEAD OF DEPARTMENT I WAS DELIGHTED WITH THE FLOOR WE'VE BEEN GIVEN AND WHAT IT SUGGESTS ABOUT HOW MUCH INCOME WE GENERATE FOR THE BANK.
BUT WE'RE ON A NON-DESCRIPT FLOOR HALFWAY UP THE BUILDING...

EXACTLY. AND I COULD SENSE MY GUYS' BONUS EXPECTATIONS SINK AS SOON AS THEY SAW THE PLANS...
FLOOR PLAN

ALEX WENT TO CORNWALL...

Alex
PEATTIE+TAYLOR
THE FORTHCOMING MOVE TO NEW PREMISES WILL GIVE THE BANK A CHANCE TO SHOW A MORE ENVIRONMENTALLY-CONSCIOUS IMAGE...
PEN
FAIR TRADE

FOR EXAMPLE, PRODUCTS USED IN THE OFFICE WILL, WHEREVER POSSIBLE, BE SOURCED FROM BIODEGRADABLE, SUSTAINABLE AND REUSABLE MATERIALS...
PEN
FAIR TRADE

AFTER ALL WE ARE CUSTODIANS OF THIS PLANET AND WE MUST BE CONSCIOUS OF NATURE'S CYCLE OF CONSTANT RENEWAL OF WHICH WE ARE ALL PART...
ABSOLUTELY...

THESE 100% RECYCLED BINLINERS WILL BE A NICE TOUCH FOR THE PRE-BONUS REDUNDANCIES...
YES... NEATLY SYMBOLISING THE TRANSITORY NATURE OF PEOPLE'S JOBS HERE.
PEN
FAIR TRADE

Alex
PEATTIE+TAYLOR
THE BANK'S NEW CORPORATE HEAD-QUARTERS WILL GIVE US THE CHANCE TO SHOW OUR GREEN CREDENTIALS...

IT IS A STATE OF THE ART BUILDING WITH SOLAR-POWERED LIGHTING, A WATER RECYCLING PLANT AND BOARDROOMS LINED WITH WOOD FROM SUSTAINABLE SOURCES...
ER... RUPERT...?

SHOULDN'T SPECIAL CONSIDERATION BE GIVEN TO THOSE OF THE BANK'S EMPLOYEES WHO HAVE ALREADY EMBRACED AN ECO-FRIENDLY LIFESTYLE? FOR EXAMPLE I DRIVE AN ELECTRIC CAR...
THAT'S A GOOD POINT...

BECAUSE: DON'T THEY GET FREE PARKING IN PUBLIC CAR PARKS?
AH YES... SO NO NEED TO GIVE HIM A PRESTIGE SPACE IN THE BANK'S CAR PARK...
ER... WAIT A MINUTE...

Alex
PEATTIE+TAYLOR
IF YOU'D JUST LIKE TO WAIT IN HERE... CAN I GET YOU ANYTHING? TEA? COFFEE...?
NO, WE'RE FINE THANKS.

TYPICAL. THE TRADITIONAL ARROGANCE OF BANKERS... THEY ALWAYS KEEP YOU WAITING...
I'M SURE IT'S JUST TO CREATE A SENSE OF THEIR OWN IMPORTANCE...

BUT THIS IS THE 21ST CENTURY. THEIRS IS A RELATIONSHIP-DRIVEN BUSINESS... WE ARE POTENTIAL CLIENTS... YOU'D THINK THEY'D TRY TO LOOK GOOD IN OUR EYES...

AS FEARED, THEY'RE WEARING DRESS DOWN, ALEX...
SIGH WHAT HAS THE WORLD COME TO? OKAY, GIMME 5 MINUTES AND I'LL CHANGE INTO MY CHINOS AND POLO SHIRT TO SUCK UP TO THEM...

Alex
PEATTIE+TAYLOR
SO, RUPERT, YOU'RE CHAIRING THE OFFICE FURNISHINGS SUB-COMMITTEE FOR THE MOVE TO THE NEW BUILDING...?
THAT'S RIGHT...

ISN'T IT A WASTE OF YOUR TIME? YOU SHOULD BE PLANNING THE BANK'S OVERALL FINANCIAL STRATEGY... ARE FIXTURES AND FITTINGS REALLY IMPORTANT?
PSYCHOLOGICALLY, YES...

OURS IS A PEOPLE BUSINESS AND IT'S MY ROLE TO REMIND STAFF THAT NO EXPENSE IS BEING SPARED TO EQUIP OUR NEW OFFICE WITH THE HIGHEST QUALITY FURNISHINGS AND DECOR...
SWIPE

SO THE BANK'S GOT LOADS OF MONEY...
BUT IT'S BLOWING IT ON POSH CARPETS...
HELL! I CAN'T WORK OUT IF MY BONUS EXPECTATIONS SHOULD BE GOING UP OR DOWN...
e-mail
e-mail
HEH, HEH... DISINFORMATION IS A POWERFUL TOOL...

Alex
PEATTIE + TAYLOR
SORRY, GUYS, I'VE GOT TO RUSH... I'VE GOT A FLIGHT BACK TO THE U.K. TO CATCH...

AS YOU KNOW I'M AN M.D. OF MY BANK, SO MY CONTRACT STIPULATES THAT I'M ALLOWED A FLAT BED ON ALL LONG DISTANCE BUSINESS TRIPS...
alex@alexcartoon.com

SO OBVIOUSLY THERE WERE VERY FEW FLIGHTS FOR ME TO CHOOSE FROM...
BUT, STEWART, FLAT BEDS ARE VERY COMMON THESE DAYS. LOADS OF PLANES ARE FITTED WITH THEM...
THAT'S TRUE...

AND INCREASINGLY SO IN BUSINESS CLASS... IT'S GETTING HARDER AND HARDER TO FIND AN AIRLINE THAT STILL ONLY DOES THEM IN FIRST
FIRST CLASS

Alex
PEATTIE + TAYLOR
THE OCTOBER CLUB
WE RAISE HUGE SUMS FROM THESE RICH CITY TYPES AT OUR CHARITY AUCTIONS... BUT ARE THEY INTERESTED IN WHAT THEIR MONEY'S SPENT ON?
DUNNO.

LOOK AT THEM BIDDING VAST AMOUNTS FOR SOME LUXURY HOLIDAY... IT'S ALL JUST AN EXCUSE TO SHOW OFF TO EACH OTHER HOW MUCH THEY CAN AFFORD, ISN'T IT?
alex@alexcartoon.com

I DON'T ACTUALLY BELIEVE THEY GIVE A DAMN ABOUT WHAT SUCH OCCASIONS ARE REALLY MEANT TO BE ABOUT, DO YOU?

WHAT, HOLIDAYS? TAKING TIME OFF WORK AND RELAXING IN THE SUN FOR A BIT?
THAT CYRUS NEVER EVEN WENT ON THE ONE HE WON LAST YEAR...

Alex
PEATTIE + TAYLOR
SO WHAT'S THIS GAME YOU GUYS PLAY?
OH IT'S JUST AN INFORMAL FANTASY FOOTBALL LEAGUE, CYRUS...
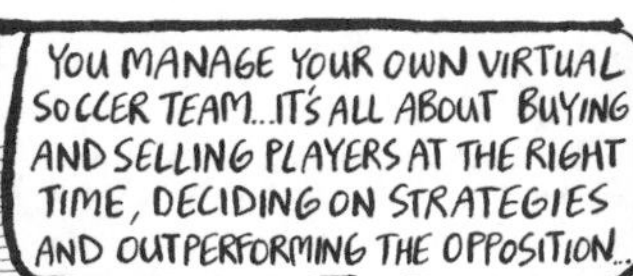
YOU MANAGE YOUR OWN VIRTUAL SOCCER TEAM... IT'S ALL ABOUT BUYING AND SELLING PLAYERS AT THE RIGHT TIME, DECIDING ON STRATEGIES AND OUTPERFORMING THE OPPOSITION...

alex@alexcartoon.com

AS HEAD OF DEPARTMENT YOU MUST BE ABLE TO SEE HOW IT'S ALL VERY RELEVANT TO OUR JOBS. I MEAN LOOK HOW WELL MY TEAM'S PERFORMING...
TAP

YOU'RE BOTTOM OF THE LEAGUE, ALEX...
EXACTLY. I JUST DON'T SEEM TO HAVE THE TIME TO DEVOTE TO IT...
HMM... WOULD ALL THIS HAVE ANYTHING TO DO WITH YOUR BONUS..?

Alex
PEATTIE + TAYLOR
IT'S BEEN MOST AMUSING WATCHING THE LATE-COMERS ARRIVING INTO WORK TODAY..

SEVERAL PEOPLE LIKE YOURSELF, JOHN HAD OBVIOUSLY FORGOTTEN THAT IT'S THE DAY OF THE OFFICE MOVE AND WERE SURPRISED TO SEE A CRATE NEXT TO YOUR DESK...
alex@alexcartoon.com

YOUR REACTION WAS PRICELESS... FOR A SPLIT-SECOND YOU THOUGHT YOU'D BEEN SACKED, DIDN'T YOU? DON'T TRY TO DENY IT... WE ALL SAW THE LOOK ON YOUR FACE...
YES...

...PURE JOY...
YOU'VE OBVIOUSLY JUST HAD A MEETING WITH A HEADHUNTER AND BEEN OFFERED A NEW JOB... AND THEN THOUGHT YOU WERE GOING TO GET A PAY-OFF FROM THIS PLACE AS WELL
SHH... DON'T TELL CYRUS.

Alex
PEATTIE+TAYLOR
THERE'S ALWAYS A CERTAIN AMOUNT OF CONFUSION AFTER A MOVE TO A NEW BUILDING...
?

NO ONE KNOWS WHERE THEY, OR ANYONE ELSE, IS SUPPOSED TO BE SITTING...
RUPERT, THIS IS RIDICULOUS...
alex@alexcartoon.com

MY TEAM AND MYSELF WERE TOLD TO REPORT TO THE 7TH FLOOR... BUT THAT'S NOT EQUITY SWAPS... IT'S OCCUPIED BY THE HUMAN RESOURCES DEPARTMENT...
AND YOUR POINT IS...?

WELL THERE'S CLEARLY BEEN A MIX UP... AS I SAY, THE 7TH FLOOR IS HUMAN RESOU-...
OH CRIPES...

I THINK THE PENNY'S DROPPED...
AN OFFICE MOVE IS ALWAYS A GOOD TIME TO SHED STAFF WITHOUT ANYONE ELSE NOTICING...
COLD SWEAT

Alex
PEATTIE+TAYLOR
STILL NO SIGN OF YOUR CRATE, CLIVE?
NO... IT'S BEEN MISLAID IN THE OFFICE MOVE...

TYPICAL INCOMPETENCE! WE'RE WORKING ON AN IMPORTANT DEAL - ADVISING A CLIENT ON ACQUIRING ANOTHER COMPANY - AND I HAVEN'T GOT ANY OF MY NOTES OR PAPERWORK...
alex@alexcartoon.com

I'M A BUSY PERSON. I DON'T HAVE TIME TO GO TRAIPSING ROUND THE BANK LOOKING FOR MY CRATE.
NO NEED, CLIVE... I THINK I KNOW WHERE IT'S ENDED UP...
REALLY? WHERE?

ER... ON OUR TRADING FLOOR... THE SHARE PRICE OF THE COMPANY OUR CLIENT IS SECRETLY PLANNING TO BUY HAS JUST SHOT UP BY 5%...
RING RING
DO YOU WANT TO TAKE THAT? I EXPECT IT'S THE CLIENT...
OH CRIPES..

Alex
PEATTIE+TAYLOR
THE WHOLE BANK IS IN TOTAL CHAOS FOLLOWING THE MOVE TO THIS NEW BUILDING TODAY...

NO ONE KNOWS WHERE THEY'RE SUPPOSED TO BE SITTING... COMPUTERS AND PHONES DON'T WORK... I'D GO AND GIVE THAT IDIOT OF A PREMISES MANAGER A PIECE OF MY MIND EXCEPT I'VE GOT NO IDEA WHERE HIS OFFICE IS...

OFFICE PLAN
alex@alexcartoon.com

CLIVE, MIGHT I REMIND YOU THAT STEVE HAS BORNE ALL THE RESPONSIBILITY FOR ORGANISING THIS COMPLEX RELOCATION... I MUST SAY I THINK YOU'RE EXAGGERATING THE SCALE OF THE PROBLEM FACED HERE...

JUST LOOK FOR THE MOST SPACIOUS, TOP FLOOR, CORNER OFFICE WITH A RIVER VIEW. THAT'LL BE HIS...
AH YES... OF COURSE... THANKS...

Alex
PEATTIE+TAYLOR
MOVING OFFICE IS ALWAYS A PECULIAR SENSATION...

EVERYONE PACKS UP THEIR STUFF ON A FRIDAY. THE TRANSPORT GUYS MOVE IT OVER THE WEEKEND AND WE ARRIVE ON MONDAY MORNING TO FIND IT ALL INSTALLED IN A NEW LOCATION.

alex@alexcartoon.com

IT ALWAYS GIVES ME A WEIRD SENSE OF DISLOCATION... YOU KNOW, SUDDENLY FINDING MYSELF IN AN ENVIRONMENT THAT IS RECOGNIZABLE, YET STRANGE AND UNFAMILIAR...
A NEW BUILDING?

ACTUALLY I MEANT MY HOUSE...
YES, IT MUST HAVE BEEN ODD FOR YOU NOT HAVING AN OFFICE TO SPEND THE WEEKEND IN FOR ONCE, CYRUS...

Alex
PEATTIE+TAYLOR
WELL, I THINK OUR ORGANISING OF THE OFFICE MOVE HAS BEEN A GREAT SUCCESS...
alex@alexcartoon.com

THANKS TO US TAKING A PHOTO OF EACH EMPLOYEE'S DESK WE WERE ABLE TO RECONSTRUCT THEIR SET-UP HERE IN THE NEW PLACE EXACTLY AS IT HAD BEEN IN THE OLD...

AN OFFICE MOVE CAN BE A TRAUMATISING EXPERIENCE AND SO IT'S IMPORTANT PEOPLE HAVE EVERYTHING THEY NEED TO FEEL COMFORTABLE AND RELAXED IN THEIR NEW ENVIRONMENT.

I STILL THINK IT WAS HORRID OF YOUR BANK TO SACK YOU UNDER COVER OF THE MOVE...
AT LEAST THEY LET ME KEEP THE PHOTO... SIGH NOW THAT WAS A REAL DESK...

Alex
PEATTIE+TAYLOR
HOW WAS THE CHARITY AUCTION, DARLING? DID YOU BUY ANYTHING?
YES, A HELICOPTER RIDE.
alex@alexcartoon.com

THAT'LL BE NICE FOR THE KIDS...
ER... ACTUALLY THIS ONE'S FOR ME... YOU SEE IT WAS MY BOSS WHO DONATED IT... IT'S HIS HELICOPTER AND HE'LL BE PILOTING IT...

WHAT?!
DON'T YOU SEE? I'LL HAVE A COUPLE OF HOURS ALONE WITH HIM TO BEND HIS EAR ABOUT MY BONUS. IT MAY HAVE COST £2,000 BUT IT'LL PAY FOR ITSELF IN THE END...

CLATTER
WHUMP
I SAID: I'VE WORKED VERY HARD THIS YEAR AND...
I'M SORRY... I STILL CAN'T HEAR YOU...

Alex
PEATTIE+TAYLOR
IT'S AN E-MAIL FROM CYRUS... HE NEEDS TO GET A TABLE AT A TOP RESTAURANT FOR LUNCH TODAY...
alex@alexcartoon.com

A BIG CLIENT IS IN TOWN AND IS INSISTING ON BEING TAKEN TO LUNCH ... WOW, WHAT AN OPPORTUNITY TO DO THE BOSS A FAVOUR IN THE RUN UP TO BONUS TIME...

WHAT A SHAME I'M UNABLE TO ASSIST HIM...
BUT, ALEX, YOU KNOW EVERY MAITRE D' IN EVERY RESTAURANT IN THE CITY...

YES, BUT I'M NOT ADMITTING THAT AT A TIME WHEN I'M TRYING TO IMPRESS ON HIM HOW HARD I'VE BEEN WORKING...
HE'S SET A TRAP FOR US, CLIVE, YOU NAIVE FOOL...

Alex
PEATTIE+TAYLOR
NIGEL, YOU'RE HEAD OF I.T... WHAT THE HELL'S GOING ON ROUND HERE?
alex@alexcartoon.com

IT'S BEEN SEVERAL DAYS SINCE WE MOVED INTO THIS NEW OFFICE AND STILL OUR COMPUTERS AND PHONES AREN'T WORKING... I'M HOLDING YOU PERSONALLY RESPONSIBLE FOR THIS.

I MEAN, DO YOU HAVE ANY CONCEPTION OF WHAT THE POTENTIAL EFFECT COULD BE ON THE BANK IF MY DEPARTMENT IS UNABLE TO FUNCTION FOR A WEEK?

ER... NONE AT ALL?
EXACTLY AND THEN THE BOARD WOULD REALISE MY PEOPLE ARE TOTALLY EXTRANEOUS AND GET RID OF US... SO SORT IT OUT...
CORPORATE COMMS
SWIPE

Alex
PEATTIE+TAYLOR
WELL, TIM, I THINK YOU HAVE A VERY STRONG CASE UNDER THIS NEW EUROPEAN DIRECTIVE ON AGEISM...
SOLICITORS AT LAW
alex@alexcartoon.com

IT IS NOW A SERIOUS OFFENCE TO SINGLE OUT ANY EMPLOYEE OR TREAT THEM DIFFERENTLY IN THE WORKPLACE ON THE GROUNDS OF THEIR AGE
I SEE...

SO YOU THINK I'VE GOT A GOOD CHANCE OF WINNING?
SURE I DO. LISTEN: WHEN WE PRESENT OUR EVIDENCE TO THE COURT IT'S GOING TO BE A PIECE OF CAKE...

THIS PIECE THAT SAYS "HAPPY 50TH TIM"?
YES. I CAN'T BELIEVE YOUR COLLEAGUES WERE SO STUPID AS TO BUY IT FOR YOU FOR YOUR BIRTHDAY LAST WEEK...

Alex
PEATTIE+TAYLOR
THESE DAYS ALL THE BANKS ARE MOVING EAST TO THE DOCKS WHILE OUR CLIENTS ARE INCREASINGLY HEADED WEST...
BAR
TAXI
alex@alexcartoon.com

BUT OBVIOUSLY WE STILL HAVE TO ENTERTAIN OUR CUSTOMERS AS WE'RE ABOUT TO DO NOW, AND MOST OF THE APPROPRIATE VENUES TEND TO BE IN THE WEST END...
HERE WE ARE, GENTS... PEPPERMINT HIPPO...
AH THANKS...

AS A RESULT WE HAVE TO SPEND A LOT MORE OF OUR LIVES TRAVELLING BACK AND FORTH IN CABS, WITH OBVIOUS CONSEQUENCES...
THAT'S £25, GUV.
HERE. KEEP THE CHANGE. CAN I HAVE A RECEIPT?

...LIKE A FEW BLANK ONES AS WELL?
...IE: IT'S MUCH EASIER TO AMASS ALL THE EXTRA TAXI RECEIPTS WE NEED FOR OUR EXPENSES...
PEPPERMINT HIPPO
TAXI
WELL THERE'S NO WAY WE CAN LEGITIMATELY CLAIM FOR LAPDANCING.

Alex
PEATTIE+TAYLOR
DID YOU SEE COLIN STAGGER INTO HIS OFFICE 5 MINUTES AGO? OBVIOUSLY JUST GOT BACK FROM LUNCH...
alex@alexcartoon.com

BUT IT'S ALMOST 5 O'CLOCK... GOODNESS KNOWS HOW DINOSAURS LIKE HIM MANAGE TO HOLD DOWN A JOB IN THE MODERN BUSINESS WORLD...

I MEAN THEY'RE TOTALLY OUT OF TOUCH WITH EVERYTHING ABOUT THE 21ST CENTURY OFFICE... WHEN IT COMES TO TECHNOLOGY THEY FIND THEMSELVES TOTALLY IN THE DARK...
YES... THEY FREQUENTLY DO

VOILA! THANKS TO THOSE SMART BULBS OUR OFFICES HAVE THAT SWITCH THEMSELVES OFF IF NO MOVEMENT IS DETECTED FOR 3 MINUTES...
HE'S CLEARLY FALLEN ASLEEP IN THERE.

Alex
PEATTIE+TAYLOR
I HEAR WE'VE APPOINTED A HEAD OF COST CUTTING...
YES. WE POACHED HIM FROM CONTINENT BANK...
alex@alexcartoon.com

HE'S GOT A TOUGH JOB TO DO TO GET THE BANK'S PROFITABILITY UP BUT APPARENTLY HE REALLY IMPRESSED AND SHOWED HIS METTLE IN THE RECRUITMENT PROCESS...

BY HIS OWN ACCOUNT HE'S A MAN WHO RESPONDS TO A CHALLENGE PROFESSIONALLY... HE LIKES TO DRIVE HIMSELF HARD AND SET THE BAR AS HIGH AS POSSIBLE...

WHICH IS WHY HE DEMANDED A MASSIVE SALARY WITH LOADS OF PERKS...
HE'S ADDED £1.5 m TO THE BANK'S COST BASE BEFORE HE'S EVEN STARTED...

Alex
PEATTIE+TAYLOR
WHY HAVE WE APPOINTED A HEAD OF COST-CUTTING? THE BANK'S MAKING LOTS OF MONEY THIS YEAR...
A NEW STRATEGY BY MANAGEMENT, CLIVE...
e-mail
e-mail

NORMALLY IT TAKES A MARKET DOWNTURN AND FALLING REVENUES BEFORE BANKS START REINING IN EXPENDITURE, AND THEN IT JUST TENDS TO EXACERBATE THE MOOD OF FEAR AND UNCERTAINTY...
e-mail
e-mail
alex@alexcartoon.com

WHEREAS OBVIOUSLY IT WILL HAVE A TOTALLY DIFFERENT EFFECT IF A ROBUST APPROACH TO COST-CUTTING IS UNDERTAKEN AT A TIME WHEN BUSINESS IS DOING WELL...
YES..

THERE ARE LOADS OF OTHER JOBS FOR ANY DISGRUNTLED STAFF TO GO TO, PLUS THE BANK WILL HAVE TO PAY OVER THE MARKET RATE TO LURE ANYONE TO REPLACE THEM...
HENCE NO COST-SAVING...NOW WHERE'S MY HEADHUNTER'S NUMBER?

Alex
PEATTIE+TAYLOR
OUR NEW HEAD OF COST CUTTING WAS POACHED FROM CONTINENT BANK, SO I PHONED MY FRIEND WHO WORKS THERE..

DID HE HAVE ANY GOSSIP?
HE SAID IT WAS PROBABLY BEST NOT TO TALK ABOUT IT ON THE PHONE BUT HE'D TELL ME ALL IF I TOOK HIM TO LUNCH.
alex@alexcartoon.com

WOW! IF HE'S HAVING TO MAKE ARRANGEMENTS LIKE THAT TO MEET YOU AWAY FROM HIS PLACE OF WORK THERE MUST BE SOMETHING PRETTY SHOCKING TO TELL...

WHAT?! HE CUT BACK YOUR LUNCH EXPENSES TO ¥25 A HEAD?!
THAT'S WHY YOU'RE PICKING UP THE TAB TODAY, ALEX... WHILE ONE OF US STILL CAN...
MENU
MENU

Alex
PEATTIE+TAYLOR
I DON'T BELIEVE IT! HAVE YOU SEEN WHAT OUR NEW HEAD OF COST CUTTING HAS DONE NOW...?

HE'S STOPPED THE PROVISION OF COFFEE IN THE BANK'S MEETING ROOMS...
HE'S ONLY DOING HIS JOB, CLIVE... ACTUALLY I THINK IT'S COMMENDABLE.
alex@alexcartoon.com

BUT, ALEX, WE SPEND HALF OUR DAY IN MEETINGS. SURELY IT'S PERFECTLY REASONABLE TO WISH TO PARTAKE OF A CUP OF COFFEE WHILE DISCUSSING BUSINESS...
ABSOLUTELY, CLIVE.

ALL MY TRIPS TO STARBUCKS TO HAVE OFF-THE-RECORD CHATS OUT OF EARSHOT OF COMPLIANCE WERE STARTING TO LOOK SUSPICIOUS... BUT NOT ANY MORE...

Alex
PEATTIE+TAYLOR
SO, THIS NEW COST-CUTTING OFFICER: THE BANK IS PAYING HIM A MILLION DOLLARS A YEAR TO SAVE MONEY?

IT MAY SEEM ODD TO US, CLIVE, BUT THIS IS THE AMERICAN WAY OF DOING BUSINESS AND WE HAVE TO RESPECT IT...
SO YOU RECKON THIS NEW GUY IS A YANK?
alex@alexcartoon.com

I EXPECT SO...FRANKLY IF YOU WANT A JOB LIKE THIS DONE EFFICIENTLY AND SINGLE-MINDEDLY, IT'S ABOUT POSSESSING CERTAIN KEY QUALITIES... AND AMERICANS TEND TO BE VERY BLESSED THAT WAY..

WITH A TOTAL ABSENCE OF A SENSE OF IRONY?
QUITE.
AT LEAST THIS CHAP WON'T BE IMPEDED BY ANY AWARENESS OF THE INHERENT CONTRADICTION IN HIS ROLE...

Alex
PEATTIE + TAYLOR
ISN'T THIS WHERE OUR NEW HEAD OF COST CUTTING HAS HIS OFFICE?
YES, CLIVE.
alex@alexcartoon.com

BUT BEING AMERICAN HE'S GIVEN HIMSELF SOME GRANDIOSE AND INPENETRABLE JOB TITLE, NO DOUBT IN ORDER TO HELP HIM ENVISION HIS CORE STRATEGIC FOCUS...

SO OFFICIALLY HE HEADS UP THE "PRODUCTIVITY AND REVENUE AMELIORIZATION TEAM"...
AMERICANS! THEY SPEAK A TOTALLY DIFFERENT LANGUAGE TO US BRITS, DON'T THEY?
YES...

P.R.A.T.
THANKFULLY...
SNIGGER
SHH...

Alex
PEATTIE + TAYLOR
OUR NEW HEAD OF COST CUTTING BELIEVES THAT THE BANK'S DAY TO DAY OFFICE EXPENDITURE CAN BE SIGNIFICANTLY REDUCED...
alex@alexcartoon.com

FOR EXAMPLE THE SAVINGS TO BE DELIVERED BY OUR SWITCHING FROM COLOUR TO BLACK AND WHITE PHOTO-COPYING COULD AMOUNT TO HUNDREDS OF THOUSANDS OF DOLLARS...

OBVIOUSLY IT'S IMPORTANT THAT ANY INTERNAL CUTBACKS SHOULD NOT BE SEEN TO AFFECT OUR PROFESSIONALISM OR THE QUALITY OF THE PRODUCTS AND SERVICES WE PROVIDE TO OUR CLIENTS...
SO HOW MUCH IS IT COSTING TO GET THE BANK'S LOGO REDESIGNED IN GREY AND REPLACE EVERYONE'S BUSINESS CARDS AND STATIONERY?
SEVERAL MILLION I EXPECT...

Alex
PEATTIE + TAYLOR
OUR NEW HEAD OF COST CUTTING IS REALLY STARTING TO MAKE HIS MARK ON THE ORGANISATION...
HE CERTAINLY IS, CLIVE...
alex@alexcartoon.com

AFTER SEVERAL BOOM YEARS RECRUITMENT AND DEPARTMENTAL SPENDING HAD SPIRALLED OUT OF CONTROL AT THE BANK... HE WAS BROUGHT IN TO SORT IT OUT.

HE'S MADE HEADCOUNT HIS FIRST PRIORITY AND DONE SOMETHING ABOUT THE NUMBERS OF NON-ESSENTIAL ADMINISTRATIVE PERSONNEL EMPLOYED IN NON-PROFIT CENTRES OF THE BANK...
YES...
HE'S INCREASED THEM CONSIDERABLY.
THE MORE COMPLEX IT BECOMES FOR ANY OF US TO GET ANY SORT OF EXPENDITURE APPROVED THE LESS LIKELY WE ARE TO BOTHER TO TRY...

Alex
PEATTIE + TAYLOR
I SEE YOU'VE TAKEN ADVANTAGE OF THE DUTY FREE, ALEX.
ALWAYS DO, CYRUS.
Arrivals
DUTY FREE
CLANK
alex@alexcartoon.com

WELL, LIQUOR FOR YOUR OWN CONSUMPTION AT HOME IS OK, I GUESS, BUT I DO NOT APPROVE OF IT IN THE WORKPLACE...
REALLY? WHY NOT?
DUTY FREE

BECAUSE, ALEX, ALCOHOL CAN HAVE A SERIOUS EFFECT ON HOW WELL AND EFFICIENTLY PEOPLE PERFORM THEIR JOBS...
I AGREE TOTALLY.
THIS BLASTED NEW COMPUTER SYSTEM'S BEEN DOWN ALL DAY... HOW COME YOUR P.C. GOT FIXED FIRST, ALEX..?
MY MONTHLY BOTTLE OF SCOTCH TO THE I.T. ENGINEER...
TAP TAP
TAP

Alex
PEATTIE + TAYLOR
SO YOU HAD AN OFF THE RECORD CHAT WITH JEREMY, OUR MINING ANALYST?
YES. I REMINDED HIM THAT HIS RESEARCH IS SUPPOSED TO BE NEUTRAL.
alex@alexcartoon.com

IF HE'S SEEN TO BE WRITING BLATANT PLUGS LIKE THIS FOR COMPANIES THAT ARE CLIENTS OF THE BANK THEN IT COULD LEAD TO AWKWARD CONSEQUENCES FOR US, THE ADVISERS TO THOSE CLIENTS.

IT'S GOOD TO SEE YOU STANDING UP FOR THE RULES FOR ONCE, ALEX.
IT'S ONLY NATURAL, CLIVE... I MEAN, IMAGINE HOW THIS RESEARCH NOTE COULD BE INTERPRETED BY THE WRONG PERSON...

SUCH AS THE CEO OF THE AUSTRALIAN MINING COMPANY IN QUESTION...
EXACTLY. HE MIGHT INVITE THE ANALYST DOWN TO THE CRICKET OUT OF GRATITUDE IN PLACE OF ONE OF US... AND THOSE ASHES TICKETS ARE LIKE GOLD DUST...

Alex
PEATTIE + TAYLOR
WHAT A WASTE OF A MORNING... BEING LECTURED BY H.R. ON THE AVOIDANCE OF AGEIST BEHAVIOUR IN THE WORKPLACE.
alex@alexcartoon.com

IT'S BEST JUST TO KEEP QUIET AT THOSE SEMINARS, CLIVE. YOU WERE ILL-ADVISED TO STAND UP AT THE END AND TELL THEM HOW ABSURD ALL THEIR NEW GUIDELINES ARE.

I JUST SAID THAT IT WAS ALL A RIDICULOUS OVER-REACTION TO THIS NEW ANTI-AGEISM LEGISLATION, SIMPLY BECAUSE NO ONE UNDERSTANDS ITS LEGAL IMPLICATIONS UNTIL IT HAS BEEN TESTED IN COURT..
TRUE.

BUT YOU SHOULDN'T HAVE REFERRED TO IT AS A "GREY AREA."
THEY'RE MAKING ME RE-DO THE COURSE TO RID MYSELF OF "NEGATIVE AGEIST STEREOTYPING" IN LANGUAGE

Alex
PEATTIE + TAYLOR
OUR NEW HEAD OF COST CUTTING WANTED TO END THE PROVISION OF FREE DIARIES TO ALL STAFF...
alex@alexcartoon.com

HE THINKS IT'S A WASTE OF MONEY AS EVERYONE HAS ELECTRONIC ORGANISERS THESE DAYS... I DISAGREED. AFTER ALL, SOME OF US PREFER A REAL DIARY...

IN THE END WE REACHED A SENSIBLE COMPROMISE. DIARIES ARE BEING SUPPLIED TO SELECT PERSONNEL ONLY, WHICH ALLOWS THE BANK TO REALISE A SIGNIFICANT COST-SAVING.
SWIPE
WHAT? JUST FROM NOT PRINTING A FEW DIARIES?

NO, BECAUSE PEOPLE ARE NOW TOO FEARFUL FOR THEIR JOBS TO WORRY ABOUT THEIR BONUSES.
WHY DIDN'T WE GET DIARIES?
OH GOD... OBVIOUSLY WE'RE NOT GOING TO BE HERE IN 2007...
2007

Alex
PEATTIE + TAYLOR
MIKE, ALL OF US IN THE NEW YORK OFFICE KNOW YOU'RE DOING A GREAT JOB AS GLOBAL HEAD OF COST-CUTTING HERE AT MEGABANK...
alex@alexcartoon.com

BUT SOME PARTS OF YOUR PROGRAM ARE QUITE CONTROVERSIAL: YOU'VE BANNED COFFEE IN MEETING ROOMS, COLOR PHOTOCOPYING, INTERNAL ENTERTAINMENT AND MOST BUSINESS TRAVEL...

THE SEVERITY OF THE CUTBACKS IS CONCERNING SOME OF US DIRECTORS BACK IN THE STATES, WHICH IS WHY I'VE MADE THIS EMERGENCY TRIP OVER TO HAVE A TALK WITH YOU...
ARE YOU HERE TO REPRIMAND ME?

NO, I'M HERE SO MY WIFE CAN DO HER CHRISTMAS SHOPPING AT HARRODS... WHICH IS MORE THAN ANYONE ELSE IS NOW PERMITTED TO DO, THANKS TO YOU...
THE OTHER WIVES ARE REALLY, REALLY UPSET WITH YOU, BY THE WAY.

Alex
PEATTIE+TAYLOR
SO, ALEX, WHERE DO YOU STAND ON THE VEIL DEBATE?
ER... YOU KNOW, I HAVEN'T REALLY BEEN FOLLOWING IT...
HIJAB
NEWS
alex@alexcartoon.com

WELL APPARENTLY IT ALL STEMS FROM AN OBLIGATION TOWARDS MODESTY IN PUBLIC WHICH DECREES THAT CERTAIN FORMS OF DRESS MUST BE ADHERED TO...
REALLY? HOW ODD.

THE BASIC REQUIREMENT IS THAT THE HEAD SHOULD BE COVERED, BUT OFTEN A GARMENT IS WORN THAT OBSCURES THE WHOLE FACE WITH JUST NARROW EYE SLITS TO LOOK OUT OF...
YES. I'VE SEEN THEM..

THOSE SKI MASKS... HOW ABSURD... IF I'VE SHELLED OUT FOR AN UPMARKET HOLIDAY ON THE SLOPES I'D WANT EVERYONE TO RECOGNISE ME....
ALEX... I'M NOT TALKING ABOUT VAIL, COLORADO...
SKI USA

Alex
PEATTIE+TAYLOR
I HATE THE WAY PEOPLE IN THE BANK CLOG UP THE E-MAIL SYSTEM WITH THESE INTERNAL GLOBAL MESSAGES...
alex@alexcartoon.com

LOOK AT THIS ONE... AS USUAL IT'S FROM SOMEONE WHO DOESN'T EVEN WORK ON THE SAME FLOOR AS US, WHO'S MISLAID SOME PETTY PERSONAL POSSESSION AND WANTS TO KNOW IF ANYONE'S SEEN IT...
IT'S TYPICAL OF HOW CERTAIN INDIVIDUALS SEEK TO APPROPRIATE THE E-MAIL SYSTEM FOR THEIR OWN PURPOSES.
OH YES. THE HEAD OF TRADING'S LOST HIS OYSTER CARD...
ER... HOLD ON...

HIS OYSTER CARD?!! A DIRECTOR OF THE BANK TAKES PUBLIC TRANSPORT?!
IGNORE IT, CLIVE. IT'S A BLATANT PLOY TO GET EVERYONE'S BONUS EXPECTATIONS DOWN.

Alex
PEATTIE+TAYLOR
IN THE NEXT PHASE OF MY COST-CUTTING PROGRAM I'M TURNING MY ATTENTION TO THE BANK'S INTERNAL MESSENGERS.
alex@alexcartoon.com

THESE PEOPLE ARE A THROWBACK TO PRE-DIGITAL DAYS WHEN PHYSICAL DOCUMENTS HAD TO BE TRANSFERRED BETWEEN DEPARTMENTS. TODAY ALL THAT STUFF IS DONE BY E-MAIL...

WE LIVE IN THE AGE OF THE INTERNET AND WE SHOULD BE ABLE TO REALIZE SIGNIFICANT COST SAVINGS BY LOOKING AT HOW MUCH ACTUAL WORK THERE IS FOR THOSE GUYS TO DO THESE DAYS..

LOADS. THEY'RE ALL RUSHED OFF THEIR FEET WITH SPECIAL DELIVERIES THAT HAVE COME TO THE BANK...
SO FIND OUT WHO THE PEOPLE ARE THAT'VE GOT NOTHING BETTER TO DO ALL DAY THAN ON-LINE SHOPPING AND FIRE THEM...
INETAPORTER
E-SHOP.COM
AMAZON

Alex
PEATTIE+TAYLOR
YOU'RE NOT REALLY GOING TO START WATCHING CRICKET AT MIDNIGHT, ALEX?
IT'S THE FIRST DAY OF THE ASHES, PENNY.
alex@alexcartoon.com

THIS IS THE ONE DAY I CAN ACTUALLY ENJOY THE CRICKET... AFTER ALL IT'S ONLY A MATTER OF TIME BEFORE ENGLAND BLOW IT...
BUT YOUR BOSS IS AN AMERICAN. HE DOESN'T KNOW OR CARE ABOUT CRICKET.

HE WON'T BE PLEASED IF YOU'RE LATE FOR WORK TOMORROW...
PENNY, THIS IS A TIME WHEN ALLOWANCES ARE MADE FOR THE CULTURAL TRADITIONS OF OTHERS, EVEN WHEN THEY ARE ALIEN TO ONE'S OWN NATION..

TOMORROW IS "THANKSGIVING" WHATEVER THAT MIGHT BE. IT'S THE ONE DAY OF THE YEAR CYRUS DOESN'T COME INTO THE OFFICE...
NOW WHERE'S THAT MAGNUM OF CLARET?

Alex
PEATTIE + TAYLOR
HAPPY THANKS-GIVING EVERYONE! NOW, LET'S ALL BOW OUR HEADS...
alex@alexcartoon.com
FOR WHAT WE ARE ABOUT TO RECEIVE MAY THE LORD MAKE US TRULY THANKFUL...
BOW
BOW
BOW
BOW
BOW
AMEN...
ER... THAT'S THE PRAYERS OVER, CYRUS...
ER, CYRUS...
TAP
TAP

Alex
PEATTIE + TAYLOR
YOUR DEPARTMENT, SIR? THEY'VE ALL GONE HOME...
MEGABANK
MEGA BANK
alex@alexcartoon.com
THEY LEFT A FEW MINUTES AFTER YOU DID AT 11-30...
HMM... SO THEY WERE JUST PRETENDING TO WORK LATE TO IMPRESS ME? RIGHT, I'M DOWNGRADING THEIR BONUSES...
DIET COKE
OH... ALL EXCEPT ALEX AND CLIVE, SIR... THEY'RE STILL UP THERE.
AFTER MIDNIGHT? OKAY, WELL I'M SERIOUSLY IMPRESSED BY THAT...
DIET COKE
WE'RE BOTH DEAD MEN WITH OUR WIVES NOW WHATEVER TIME WE GET HOME...
QUITE... SO WE MIGHT AS WELL ENJOY THE CRICKET FROM AUSTRALIA HERE IN PEACE...

Alex
PEATTIE + TAYLOR
AH, MIKE... THANKS FOR DROPPING IN... I NEED TO REVIEW YOUR ROLE AS THE BANK'S HEAD OF COST CUTTING...
RUPERT TERLING DIRECTOR
alex@alexcartoon.com
THOUGH WE'VE BEEN HAILING YOU AS A GREAT SUCCESS, IN FACT YOUR POLICIES HAVE JUST HACKED OFF OUR STAFF AND CAUSED THEM TO RESIGN EN MASSE.
SO I'M AFRAID THE BOARD HAS NO OPTION BUT TO TERMINATE YOUR EMPLOYMENT HERE.
WHAT?! BUT, RUPERT...
P45
THERE WERE STILL WAYS I COULD HAVE SAVED MONEY FOR THE BANK... IF ONLY YOU'D GIVEN ME MORE TIME...
P45
AND HOW MUCH LONGER DID YOU NEED?
ABOUT ANOTHER 30 SECONDS... I'D COME TO TELL YOU I'VE BEEN HEADHUNTED...
SO WE COULD HAVE SAVED PAYING YOU A SETTLEMENT?
BLAST!
P45

Alex
PEATTIE + TAYLOR
IT MADE SENSE TO GET RID OF OUR HEAD OF COST-CUTTING YESTERDAY.
alex@alexcartoon.com
FRANKLY WE'D ALREADY ASSIMILATED HIS METHODS: BANNING FREE COFFEE, RATIONING STATIONERY, INSTALLING LOW WATTAGE LIGHTING ETC...
HIS POLICIES SAVED THE BANK HALF A MILLION POUNDS...
YES, BUT WE HAD TO GIVE HIM ¥250,000 SEVERANCE PAY...
AND HOW MUCH DID OUR TRADING DESK LOSE ON JAPANESE DERIVATIVES YESTERDAY?
¥100m...
BUT THERE'S A FULL ENQUIRY UNDERWAY...
THE HEAD OF THE DESK HAD POPPED OUT TO STARBUCKS TO GET HIS CAFFEINE HIT...
I COULDN'T WORK OUT THE TRADE AS THE PROPS DESK HAD BORROWED THE ONLY CALCULATOR...
AND I HIT THE WRONG BUTTON IN THE HALF-LIGHT.
SIGH

Alex
PEATTIE + TAYLOR
THE WAY THIS NEW DIRECTIVE ON AGEISM IS BEING INTERPRETED BY H.R. IS LUDICROUS..

EARLY RETIREMENT CAN NO LONGER BE OFFERED UNLESS MADE AVAILABLE TO ALL STAFF, INCLUDING GRADUATE TRAINEES, AND WE CAN'T ADVERTISE FOR A "SENIOR ANALYST" IN CASE YOUNG PEOPLE FEEL DISCRIMINATED AGAINST...
alex@alexcartoon.com

FRANKLY THIS LEGISLATION SEEMS TO WORK EXCLUSIVELY FOR THE BENEFIT OF YOUNGSTERS LIKE CHRISTIAN OVER THERE RATHER THAN US OLDER PEOPLE.
NOT ENTIRELY, CLIVE...

OH, CHRISTIAN... YOU'VE BEEN CHOSEN TO PLAY SANTA AT THE BANK'S KIDS' CHRISTMAS PARTY NEXT WEEK...
EH? WHAT?...
NO WAY...
WELL ANYONE OVER 40 COULD SUE THE BANK FOR AGEIST STEREOTYPING...

Alex
PEATTIE + TAYLOR
MY NEW CREDIT CARD IS REALLY GOING TO IMPRESS MY PEERS IN THE BUSINESS WORLD...
SIGH

THE GOLD, PLATINUM AND EVEN THE BLACK ONES ARE TOTALLY PASSÉ NOW... THIS NEW MUST-HAVE CARD FOR THE HIGH SPENDER IS ACTUALLY CRAFTED OUT OF TITANIUM...
SO WHAT?
alex@alexcartoon.com

HOW'S IT ANY DIFFERENT TO IF IT WAS JUST MADE OUT OF STANDARD PLASTIC? I MEAN CREDIT CARDS ONLY GET SEEN BY THE OCCASIONAL WAITER OR SHOP ASSISTANT...

SO: IT'S NOT COINS, KEYS OR YOUR BELT BUCKLE... DO YOU HAVE ANYTHING ELSE METALLIC ON YOU, SIR?
AH... OH YES! SO I DO! SORRY TO HOLD YOU UP EVERYBODY...
BEEP

Alex
PEATTIE + TAYLOR
NEXT THURSDAY AT 3:30...? YES, THAT'S GOOD.. WE'LL MEET THEN...
FLIP
I CAN'T BELIEVE YOU STILL HAVE THAT OLD-FASHIONED PAPER DIARY, ALEX...

NOWADAYS OUR WHOLE DEPARTMENT HAS ACCESS TO AN ONLINE DIARY, SHARED ON A NETWORK, WHICH AUTOMATICALLY SYNCHS UP WITH ONE'S P.C. AND BLACKBERRY...
I LIKE MY DIARY, CLIVE.
2007
alex@alexcartoon.com

BUT CAN'T YOU SEE THE DIFFERENCE TO ONE'S BUSINESS EFFICIENCY OF BEING ON A PAPERLESS INTRANET-BASED SYSTEM RATHER THAN HAVING A BULKY PHYSICAL DIARY YOU HAVE TO LUG AROUND?
OF COURSE I CAN...

OH WHAT?!! I WAS ONLY OUT OF THE OFFICE FOR AN HOUR AND OTHER PEOPLE HAVE FILLED UP MY DIARY WITH MEETINGS FOR THE REST OF THE AFTERNOON...
NOT MINE...
TAP TAP
2007

Alex
PEATTIE + TAYLOR
DECEMBER'S HARDLY STARTED AND ALREADY I CAN FEEL A SENSE OF ANTICLIMAX SETTING IN...

I'D BEEN LOOKING FORWARDS TO OVER-INDULGING ON BOOZE AND FOOD, SPENDING HOURS IN FRONT OF THE TELLY...
I SUPPOSE WITH ALL THE HYPE AND BUILD UP IT CAN NEVER REALLY LIVE UP TO EXPECTATIONS...
alex@alexcartoon.com

AND ALL THOSE TRADITIONAL THINGS THAT USED TO MAKE IT SPECIAL THAT WE DON'T HAVE ANY MORE... LIKE SLEDGING.
YES...

WELL ENGLAND ARE SO ABJECTLY USELESS THAT THE AUSSIES DON'T NEED TO DO THAT STUFF ANY MORE...
G'DAY MATE. HAVE A NICE INNINGS...
SHALL WE JUST SWITCH THE ASHES OFF AND GET SOME SLEEP?

Alex
PEATTIE + TAYLOR
SO, YOU HAVE A PRIVATE EQUITY COMPANY THAT WANTS TO BUY MY BUSINESS?
GLOBAL HEADQU
XMAS INC
YES, WITH A VIEW TO FLOATING IT IN A FEW YEARS...
alex@alexcartoon.com

WELL, I'D NEED REASSURING THAT THEY WOULDN'T MAKE TOO MANY CHANGES...
ABSOLUTELY. EXCEPT WE'D PROBABLY OUTSOURCE THE TOY-MAKING, THE LETTER ANSWERING AND THE DELIVERY OF THE PRESENTS...

WHAT?!! THERE'LL BE NOTHING LEFT HERE! SURELY YOU DON'T WANT TO GET RID OF MY COMPANY HQ...?
MR CLAUS, IT'S IN THE MIDDLE OF NOWHERE.. IT'S COLD, REMOTE, INHOSPITABLE...

IN OTHER WORDS THE PERFECT PLACE TO HOLD THE A.G.M...
NONE OF THE SMALL SHARE-HOLDERS WILL BOTHER TO TRUDGE OUT TO LAPLAND...

Alex
PEATTIE + TAYLOR
SO YOUR PRIVATE EQUITY COMPANY IS PROPOSING TO BUY MY BUSINESS AND THEN GET IT INTO DEBT?
OBAL HEADQUARTERS OF XMAS INC
alex@alexcartoon.com

LOOK, MR CLAUS, IT'S ALL VERY QUAINT AND TRADITIONAL UP HERE IN LAPLAND BUT IF WE'RE TO TURN YOUR COMPANY ROUND WE NEED TO FINANCE MAJOR WORKS...

ONCE WE FLOAT THE BUSINESS THE CITY ANALYSTS WILL BE COMING HERE ON SITE VISITS... THEIR APPROVAL IS VITAL TO YOUR SUCCESS BUT THEY'LL BE VERY DEMANDING...
I SUPPOSE MY WORKSHOP COULD USE SOME MODERNISATION...

ACTUALLY WE WERE THINKING IN TERMS OF PUTTING IN A SKI-LIFT AND A FEW CHALETS...
FOB THEM OFF WITH A BIT OF R&R AND THEY'LL TURN A BLIND EYE TO THE REST...

Alex
PEATTIE + TAYLOR
THIS HAS GOT TO BE ONE OF THE BEST PRIVATE EQUITY DEALS EVER – BUYING UP SANTA CLAUS'S OPERATION...
GLOBAL HEADQU OF XMAS IN
alex@alexcartoon.com

I MEAN CHRISTMAS IS ONE OF THE BIGGEST FRANCHISES IN THE WORLD. WE'VE ALL KNOWN AND LOVED THE EXCITEMENT AND MYSTIQUE OF IT SINCE WE WERE KIDS...

WE ALL KNOW THE FEELING OF WRITING THAT ALL-IMPORTANT BUT SECRET LETTER THAT NO ONE MUST SEE – AND MAKING SURE IT'S PUT IN THE RIGHT PLACE...
YES WE DO...
TAP TAP

THE LAST-MINUTE LETTER EXPRESSING ONE'S MISGIVINGS ABOUT THE DEAL, WHICH ONE PUTS IN THE BACK OF THE FILE TO COVER ONE'S BOTTOM AND IT ONLY GETS READ IF THINGS GO WRONG LATER AND OUR BOSSES OPEN IT UP TO INVESTIGATE
I'M WRITING MINE NOW.

Alex
PEATTIE + TAYLOR
AS PART OF THE DUE DILIGENCE PROCESS WE NEED TO DO AN INVENTORY OF ALL SANTA'S COMPANY'S ASSETS...
alex@alexcartoon.com

AS WE'LL BE OUTSOURCING THE DELIVERY OF PRESENTS WE'RE NOT GOING TO NEED THE SLEIGH, THE TEAM OF REINDEER OR THAT STUPID RED SUIT...
SO WE SELL THEM OFF?
JOT JOT

NO, THEY'RE NOT WORTH MUCH BUT THEY'RE PROBABLY OF SENTIMENTAL VALUE TO SANTA, WE'LL LET HIM HAVE THEM TO SOFTEN THE BLOW OF WHAT WE'RE DOING TO HIM...
RIGHTY-HO. SO DOES HE GET THE SACK TOO?

YES, BUT WE'LL DISGUISE IT AS PROMOTION TO NON-EXECUTIVE CHAIRMAN...
OKAY..

Alex
PEATTIE + TAYLOR
YOU PEOPLE ARE RUINING MY COMPANY...
WE'RE JUST TRYING TO MAKE IT INTO A VIABLE 21ST CENTURY BUSINESS...

BUT YOU'VE MOVED ALL MY ELVES INTO GRATUITOUS MIDDLE OFFICE ROLES WITH MEANINGLESS JOB TITLES WHERE THEY SPEND ALL DAY HAVING MEETINGS WITH EACH OTHER INSTEAD OF MAKING TOYS...

alex@alexcartoon.com

WHAT DO I WANT WITH A WHOLE FLOOR FULL OF H.R. PEOPLE WHEN DOWN IN THE WORKSHOP I'M SERIOUSLY SHORT-STAFFED?

WE MUST AVOID EXPRESSIONS LIKE "SHORT-STAFFED", MR CLAUS, WHICH MAY GIVE OFFENCE TO PERSONS OF ALTERNATIVE VERTICAL ALIGNMENT...
DIVERSITY SEMINAR

Alex
PEATTIE + TAYLOR
SO THE NEXT STEP IN TURNING ROUND SANTA'S COMPANY IS TO FIRE ALL HIS DIRECTORS AND APPOINT OUR OWN PEOPLE TO THE BOARD...

alex@alexcartoon.com
NOT FORGETTING TO INCLUDE SOME NON-EXECUTIVE DIRECTORS.
NON-EXECS ARE A WASTE OF SPACE, CLIVE. ...THEY'LL JUST STOP US RUNNING THE COMPANY AS WE WANT TO...

BUT, ALEX, WE CAN'T BE SEEN TO BE IGNORING THE RECOMMENDATIONS MADE BY THE CADBURY REPORT... SIR ADRIAN CADBURY IS STILL A RESPECTED FIGURE IN THE WORLD OF CORPORATE GOVERNANCE...

OKAY... GET HIM ON THE PHONE AND ASK HIM TO EXEMPT US... THE CONFECTIONERY FRANCHISE ON A BUSINESS LIKE THIS HAS GOT TO BE WORTH SOMETHING TO HIM...

Alex
PEATTIE + TAYLOR
THE NEW OWNERS OF YOUR COMPANY WILL NEED TO REASSESS YOUR BUSINESS MODEL, MR CLAUS...

alex@alexcartoon.com
AS WE UNDERSTAND IT YOU GO ROUND ON A SLEIGH ON CHRISTMAS EVE, CLIMB DOWN CHIMNEYS AND DELIVER PRESENTS TO CHILDREN ALL OVER THE WORLD...
YES. THE KIDS LOVE IT... THE PARENTS ARE ALWAYS VERY GRATEFUL...

WITH ALL DUE RESPECT, MR CLAUS, YOU CAN'T RUN A BUSINESS LIKE THAT IN THE 21ST CENTURY. WE WILL HAVE TO INSIST ON EXTENSIVE MODERNISATION OF YOUR PROCEDURES...

OK... I MAKE THAT 18,746,103 MINCE PIES AND 23,692,581 GLASSES OF SHERRY LAST YEAR...
NOW ENTER IT ALL AS "HOSPITALITY" IN YOUR COMPLIANCE DECLARATION.

Alex
PEATTIE + TAYLOR
WHAT ARE YOUR PRIVATE EQUITY PEOPLE DOING TO MY BUSINESS, ALEX? THEY'VE OUTSOURCED ALL MY ELVES' JOBS TO ASIA...

alex@alexcartoon.com
WE NEED TO KEEP COSTS DOWN AND TAKE ADVANTAGE OF THE BETTER WAGE CONDITIONS THAT WE CAN GET IN INDIA AND VIETNAM, MR CLAUS...
GOOD GRIEF!

HOW CAN YOU OUTSOURCE CHRISTMAS TO THE FAR EAST? THE PEOPLE OUT THERE ARE MAINLY HINDUS AND BUDDHISTS...
EXACTLY..

SO WE DON'T HAVE TO PAY THEM TRIPLE TIME FOR WORKING THE CHRISTMAS WEEKEND...

Alex
PEATTIE + TAYLOR
SO YOU'RE REPLACING MY ELVES' WORKSHOP WITH ASSEMBLY LINES IN THE FAR EAST THAT PROBABLY EXPLOIT CHILD LABOUR?
XMAS INC
HOLD ON, MR CLAUS...
alex@alexcartoon.com

WE'RE NOT MONSTERS OF THE VICTORIAN INDUSTRIAL AGE... WE WANT TO WORK WITHIN THE MODERN LAWS WITH REGARD TO HUMAN RIGHTS, ETHICAL EMPLOYMENT STANDARDS AND UNDER-AGE WORKERS...

WE BELIEVE THERE'S A UNIQUE OPPORTUNITY TO SET AN EXAMPLE OF THIS BECAUSE OF YOUR WORK AND THE NAME AND REPUTATION YOU'VE ESTABLISHED, MR CLAUS...
FOR BEING A PHILANTHROPIST?

NO, FOR GOING UP AND DOWN CHIMNEYS...
WE'RE RETRAINING THE ELVES AS MINI-SWEEPS. THEY'RE JUST THE RIGHT SIZE.
COME ON... UP YOU GO...

Alex
PEATTIE + TAYLOR
MY PRIVATE EQUITY CLIENTS ARE DELIGHTED WITH THE WAY WE'VE RESTRUCTURED YOUR COMPANY, MR CLAUS...
WELL, I'M NOT.
alex@alexcartoon.com

YOU'VE OUTSOURCED EVERYTHING IN MY BUSINESS AND LEFT NOTHING FOR ME TO DO...
I'M SURE WE CAN FIND YOU SOMETHING. WHAT EXACTLY ARE YOUR SKILLS?

MY SKILLS?!! ONLY DELIVERING GIFTS TO PEOPLE'S HOMES AT CHRISTMAS! BUT I SUPPOSE THERE'S NO ROLE FOR SOMEONE LIKE ME IN TODAY'S CORPORATE BUSINESS WORLD, IS THERE?
OH DON'T BE SO SURE...

AH, THANKS, SANTA... I WOULDN'T WANT MY XMAS PRESENTS FROM MY GRATEFUL CLIENTS TO ARRIVE AT THE BANK AND THEN HAVE TO BE DECLARED TO COMPLIANCE...
WINE
KRUG

Alex
PEATTIE + TAYLOR
THIS IS WHERE THE ELVES USED TO SIT WHO OPENED ALL THE LETTERS KIDS SENT TO ME...
alex@alexcartoon.com

LOOK, MR CLAUS, THAT WHOLE PROCESS IS BEING FAR MORE EFFICIENTLY HANDLED NOW WE'VE OUTSOURCED IT ALL TO AN OFFICE IN BANGALORE...

YOU GET MILLIONS OF LETTERS FROM CHILDREN SAYING WHAT THEY WANT FOR CHRISTMAS. WITH A MODERN DATABASING SYSTEM WE CAN ENSURE EACH CHILD GETS A PERSONALISED RESPONSE...

IN THE FORM OF PRECISELY TARGETED JUNK MAIL AND SPAM... WE'RE MAKING A FORTUNE SELLING THE INFORMATION ON TO DIRECT MARKETING COMPANIES...

Alex
PEATTIE + TAYLOR
NOW THE PROBLEM WITH YOUR BUSINESS MODEL IS THAT YOU ONLY WORK ONE DAY A YEAR...
alex@alexcartoon.com

TO GET THIS COMPANY PROFITABLE WE NEED TO EXPAND TO AN ALL-YEAR-ROUND OPERATION...
BUT, ALEX, MY WORK IS TO LEAVE LITTLE GIFTS FOR CHILDREN WHILE THEY SLEEP...

...YOU DON'T NEED FINANCIAL REWARDS TO MAKE A JOB LIKE THAT WORTHWILE... YOU JUST NEED TO SEE THE SMILE ON A SIX-YEAR-OLD CHILD'S FACE...
A SIX-YEAR-OLD'S SMILE...? HMM...

THIS IS WHAT GAVE ME THE IDEA OF HEADHUNTING THE TOOTH FAIRY TO RUN THIS BUSINESS...
BRILLIANT! HER OPERATION IS 365 DAYS A YEAR...
AND A FEMALE CEO WILL LOOK GOOD TO THE MARKETS...

ALEX IS RESTRUCTURING CHRISTMAS...

HEAD
COUNT
REDUCT
ION

!

HO HO HO
P45
HO?
NEW VIETNAM HQ OF XMAS INC.
I.D. PASS

Alex
PEATTIE + TAYLOR
IN SOME WAYS I'M GLAD YOU PEOPLE BOUGHT MY COMPANY FROM ME... CHRISTMAS DOESN'T SEEM TO HAVE THE SAME UNIVERSAL SIGNIFICANCE IT USED TO...
XMAS INC.

INDEED, MR CLAUS... TRADITIONAL CHRISTIAN FAITH IS IN A DECLINE AND WE NEED TO REACH OUT TO OTHER PEOPLE OF DIFFERENT RELIGIOUS BELIEFS THESE DAYS...
alex@alexcartoon.com

MAYBE... BUT IT SEEMS RIDICULOUS THAT WE'RE NOT EVEN ALLOWED TO SAY THE WORD "CHRISTMAS" BUT HAVE TO USE SOME STUPID EUPHEMISM INSTEAD...
IT'S A NECESSARY MEASURE...

"CHESTNUT" IS OUR CODE NAME FOR YOUR COMPANY IN THE SECRET TAKEOVER BID WE'RE MOUNTING FOR THE FESTIVAL OF YOM KIPPUR...
OR "PRETZEL" AS WE'RE CALLING IT...

Alex
PEATTIE + TAYLOR
YOU'D THINK SANTA WOULD BE GRATEFUL THAT WE'VE LET HIM STAY ON AS NON-EXECUTIVE CHAIRMAN OF HIS COMPANY.
XMAS INC.

WELL, WE HAD TO GIVE HIM SOME TOKEN ROLE. AFTER ALL HIS IMAGE IS CRUCIAL TO THE BUSINESS HE SET UP WHICH WE'VE BOUGHT OFF HIM WITH A VIEW TO FLOATING...
alex@alexcartoon.com

STILL, ONE CAN UNDERSTAND HIS FEELINGS. IT MUST BE HARD TO HAVE TO DIVEST ONESELF OF SOMETHING THAT ONE HAS GROWN OVER SUCH A LONG PERIOD OF TIME...
S. CLAUS CHAIRMAN

HIS BEARD? YES, HE WASN'T HAPPY ABOUT BEING TOLD TO SHAVE IT OFF...
DIRECTORS WITH FACIAL HAIR ARE A REAL NO-NO TO INVESTORS...

Alex
PEATTIE + TAYLOR
EVEN IN THE ARCTIC CIRCLE, ALEX... 3 NIGHTS IN A ROW WATCHING TEDIOUS NATIVE PAGEANTS..?
YAWN...
BONG BONG
JINGLE
STOMP
AH, BUT IT'S A LEGITIMATE PART OF OUR CLIENT ENTERTAINING, CLIVE...

AND THERE'S SOMETHING VERY UNIQUE ABOUT THIS EXPERIENCE WHICH I SHALL BE GLAD TO BE TAKING BACK WITH ME TO MY LIFE IN THE U.K....
BONG BONG BONG
REALLY?
alex@alexcartoon.com

YES, I SEE IT AS AN OPPORTUNITY TO SAVOUR A TIME-HONOURED RITUAL, PLAYED OUT ACCORDING TO TRADITIONAL RULES BUT STILL GIVING SCOPE FOR INDIVIDUAL SELF-EXPRESSION AND FLAIR...
BOW
CLAP CLAP CLAP
?

WHAT ARE ALL THESE EXPENSES RECEIPTS FOR, ALEX?
ER, LAPP DANCING, RUPERT.
WHA-AT!! I SHALL SEE YOU SACKED FOR THIS!
OH, I DON'T THINK YOU WILL, RUPERT...

Alex
PEATTIE + TAYLOR
ALEX! YOU SLEPT IN THE ARMCHAIR!
WHA-? OH... I MUST HAVE DOZED OFF IN FRONT OF THE TV...

ALL THAT STUFF ABOUT TAKING OVER SANTA CLAUS'S COMPANY... IT WAS ALL A DREAM...
YOU HAD A DREAM ABOUT SANTA, ALEX?
alex@alexcartoon.com

LOOK, PENNY, SOMETIMES WE ADULTS NEED TO ESCAPE FROM THE HARSH REALITIES OF OUR EVERYDAY EXISTENCE...

WE ALL HAVE AN INNER CHILD THAT LIKES TO CLING TO AN IDEALISED WORLD AND CONSOLE ITSELF WITH COMFORTING MYTHS...
THAT SANTA EXISTS?

NO, THAT ENGLAND MIGHT RETAIN THE ASHES ...THANK GOD I SLEPT THROUGH MOST OF THAT DEBACLE...
Teletext ASHES AUS 5 ENG 0

Alex
PEATTIE + TAYLOR
SO WHAT DID ALEX GET YOU FOR CHRISTMAS, PENNY...?
THIS ANYA HINDMARCH HANDBAG.
alex@alexcartoon.com

AMAZING...IS THAT THE SPECIAL EDITION VERSION IN REAL CALF'S LEATHER THAT CONTAINS A PERSONALISED DEDICATION FROM THE PERSON IT'S A PRESENT FROM?
YES.

THE GIVER HAND-WRITES A MESSAGE WHICH GETS SCANNED ON A COMPUTER AND THEN A FACSIMILE OF IT IS EMBOSSED IN GOLD INSIDE THE BAG...THAT REALLY SHOWS HOW PERSONAL THE GIFT IS, DOESN'T IT?
YES...

IT'S ALEX'S SECRETARY'S HANDWRITING...
AH...

Alex
PEATTIE + TAYLOR
GOOD NEWS IN OUR BID TO POACH FIFTY KEY INDIVIDUALS FROM OUR ARCH RIVALS CONTINENT BANK...
alex@alexcartoon.com

WE'VE MANAGED TO PERSUADE ONE OF THE MOST IMPORTANT PEOPLE ON OUR WISH LIST TO DEFECT TO US...I'M ON MY WAY TO OFFER MY MY CONGRATULATIONS PERSONALLY.

AND TO SAY HOW DELIGHTED I AM THAT THIS PERSON WILL BE BRINGING THEIR SKILLS, KNOWLEDGE AND EXPERTISE TO MEGABANK...
BUT ISN'T SHE JUST A JUNIOR MEMBER OF THEIR H.R. DEPT?
YES..

SO YOU KNOW HOW MUCH YOUR EX-COLLEAGUES ACTUALLY GET PAID AND THE REAL SIZE OF THEIR BONUSES LAST YEAR?
OF COURSE I DO...
GOOD...THAT'LL SAVE US A FORTUNE WHEN IT COMES TO NEGOTIATING THEIR SALARY PACKAGES HERE...

Alex
PEATTIE + TAYLOR
I'M AFRAID ANOTHER OF OUR SENIOR PEOPLE HAS BEEN POACHED BY OUR ARCH-RIVAL MEGABANK...
CONTINENT BANK
alex@alexcartoon.com

WE HAVE TO DECIDE WHETHER TO ALLOW HIM TO START WORK THERE STRAIGHT AWAY OR FORCE HIM TO SIT OUT HIS CONTRACT AT HOME ON 3 MONTHS' "GARDENING LEAVE"...

WELL, HE'S ONE OF THE TOP AND MOST ABLE PEOPLE IN HIS FIELD... IMAGINE HIM STARTING WORK FOR A DIRECT COMPETITOR NEXT WEEK...

AND STOPPING THEM DOING ANY DEALS IN HIS CAPACITY AS HEAD OF COMPLIANCE? YES PLEASE!
SO: WE RELEASE HIM IMMEDIATELY?

Alex
PEATTIE + TAYLOR
SO YOU HAVEN'T GIVEN UP DRINKING FOR JANUARY, ALEX?
NO, I'M NOT BOTHERING THIS YEAR...
alex@alexcartoon.com

OF COURSE MY JOB INVOLVES A GOOD DEAL OF LUNCHING AND I NORMALLY GIVE MY LIVER A BREAK IN THE NEW YEAR, BUT IT'S NOT VERY PRACTICABLE WITH THE NEW BOSS I'VE GOT...

CYRUS? BUT SURELY HE'S A PURITANNICAL AND RABIDLY TEETOTAL AMERICAN...?

EXACTLY. AND IF MY EXPENSES CLAIM TOOK A SHARP DIP IN JANUARY HE'D BE ABLE TO CALCULATE HOW MUCH OF IT HABITUALLY GOES ON BOOZE...

Alex
PEATTIE + TAYLOR
THANKS. TALK TO YOU SOON. BYE.
ALEX REALLY IS A BANKER AFTER MY OWN HEART IN MANY WAYS.

A LOT OF ENGLISH GUYS WANT TO DAWDLE ON THE PHONE, MAKING SMALL TALK, CRACKING JOKES, WASTING TIME EXCHANGING BANTER AND GOSSIP WITH CLIENTS...

BUT NOT ALEX...
alex@alexcartoon.com

DID YOU SEE THE WAY HE JUST PICKED UP THE PHONE, GOT STRAIGHT DOWN TO BUSINESS, DISCUSSED THE PARTICULARS OF THE DEAL AND THEN POLITELY WOUND UP THE CONVERSATION...?

SO YOU MANAGED TO SPEAK TO AN AUSTRALIAN CLIENT WITHOUT HIM MENTIONING THE CRICKET?!!
I DIDN'T GIVE HIM A CHANCE.

Alex
PEATTIE + TAYLOR
DID YOU SEE THIS PIECE IN THE "BUGLE" ABOUT CITY BONUSES?
OH YES. THE PAPERS ARE FULL OF STORIES ON THAT RIGHT NOW...

APPARENTLY AVERAGE LEVELS ARE EXPECTED TO BE UP BY 20% THIS YEAR...
WELL! I'M BETTER THAN AVERAGE SO THAT MEANS MY BONUS SHOULD BE UP BY 30%...
YES. MINE TOO...
alex@alexcartoon.com

I WONDER WHERE THEY GET THESE FIGURES FROM...
OH NO DOUBT THEY HAVE ACADEMICS AND STATISTICIANS PORING OVER COMPANY ACCOUNTS AND OTHER OFFICIAL DATA...

HI. I'M FROM THE "ECHO" AND I'M COMPILING STATISTICS FOR A FEATURE ON CITY BONUSES... DO YOU EXPECT YOURS TO BE UP OR DOWN ON LAST YEAR?
UP BY 30%...
YES. ME TOO.

Alex
PEATTIE + TAYLOR
THE FINANCIAL WORLD IS A TOTALLY DIFFERENT PLACE TO THE ONE WE JOINED 20 YEARS AGO...
IT CERTAINLY IS...

BACK THEN IT WAS MORE FORMAL - IN THAT PEOPLE USED TO DRESS PROPERLY FOR BUSINESS - BUT AT THE SAME TIME IT WAS MORE RELAXED AND LIGHT-HEARTED...

YES... WE USED TO HAVE A LAUGH...

OF COURSE WE STILL PLAY THE OLD-FASHIONED JAPES ON NEW RECRUITS. WHEN SYLVAIN THERE JOINED US 2 WEEKS AGO, WE PUT HIS TIE THROUGH THE SHREDDER ON HIS FIRST DAY...
HEE HEE YES...

...AND HE'S ONLY JUST REALISED...
WHO DID THIS?! I'VE GOT A CLIENT MEETING I HAVE TO WEAR IT FOR IN 2 MINUTES...
THE DRESS DOWN ERA DOES HAVE SOME ADVANTAGES...

Alex
PEATTIE + TAYLOR
I HEAR OUR HEAD OF TRADING WAS HAULED OVER THE COALS BY H.R...
WHAT FOR?

"USE OF INAPPROPRIATE LANGUAGE" IN DISCIPLINING ONE OF HIS TRADERS WHO'S NOW CONSIDERING SUING THE BANK...
ONE'S GOT TO BE SO CAREFUL THESE DAYS...
alex@alexcartoon.com

EXACTLY. ONE MUST NOT BE SEEN TO BE DISCRIMINATING AGAINST ANY SOCIAL GROUPS ON GROUNDS OF GENDER, RACE, SEXUALITY, AGE, OR EVEN BODY MASS INDEX...

SO WHAT DOES ONE DO WHEN A TRADER HITS THE WRONG BUTTON ON HIS COMPUTER AND LOSES THE BANK £15 MILLION?
SACK HIM FOR INCOMPETENCE BY ALL MEANS BUT DON'T REFER TO IT AS A "FAT FINGER" TRADE...

Alex
PEATTIE + TAYLOR
OH MY GOSH, CYRUS. YOU JUST SKIED INTO A RAVINE... ARE YOU OKAY?
YEAH, BUT I CAN'T MOVE...

WE'LL HAVE TO STAY HERE AND WAIT FOR MOUNTAIN RESCUE... BUT THEY COULD BE HOURS...
I KNOW...

YOU'RE GOING TO BE OKAY, CYRUS... IF YOU FOLLOW THE SIMPLE RULES: DON'T PANIC; DON'T LOSE BODY HEAT...
YEAH...? YEAH...?

AND GUARD AGAINST THE RISK OF EXPOSURE...
JEEZ!!
alex@alexcartoon.com

TO MARKET FLUCTUATIONS! OF COURSE! THANKS FOR REMINDING ME... NOW, IF I CAN GET THESE GODDAM GLOVES OFF, THEN I CAN CHECK THE SHARE PRICES ON MY BLACKBERRY...
TUG
FUMBLE

Alex
PEATTIE + TAYLOR
I CAN SEE THE LEDGE WHERE YOU'RE LYING, CYRUS... IT'S ABOUT 50 FEET DOWN THE RAVINE...
alex@alexcartoon.com

I'M GOING TO TRY TO CLIMB DOWN TO GET TO YOU...
NO, ALEX, DON'T DO THAT.. WAIT FOR THE MOUNTAIN RESCUE SERVICE TO ARRIVE...

THEY COULD BE HOURS, CYRUS, AND IN THE MEANTIME YOU'RE TRAPPED DOWN THERE, ALONE, HELPLESS AND UNABLE TO MOVE... I CAN'T JUST STAY UP HERE...

...SO I WANTED TO MENTION HOW HARD I'VE WORKED THIS YEAR AND TO HOPE MY BONUS WILL REFLECT THIS...
CAN'T WE SAVE THIS TILL ANOTHER TIME, ALEX?

Alex
PEATTIE + TAYLOR
STILL NO SIGN OF RESCUE, CYRUS.. YOU REALISE WE COULD BE DOOMED TO DIE HERE?
YES...
alex@alexcartoon.com

BUT LYING HERE AWAITING MY FATE I FEEL A STRANGE SENSE OF PEACE... I HAVE TIME TO MYSELF FOR THE FIRST TIME IN YEARS...

I FEEL THE LIFTING OF AN INVISIBLE WEIGHT THAT'S BEEN PUSHING DOWN ON ME... THERE'S A SENSE OF RENEWAL... OF WIPING THE SLATE CLEAN, OF LIBERATION...
I KNOW WHAT YOU MEAN...

ALL THOSE UNREAD E-MAILS SITTING IN ONE'S INBOX...
IT'S GREAT TO BE ABLE TO FINALLY GO THROUGH THEM AND DELETE THEM ALL..

Alex
PEATTIE + TAYLOR
I DON'T KNOW HOW TO SAY THIS, CYRUS, BUT THERE'S A CHANCE THAT ONE OR BOTH OF US MAY NOT PULL THROUGH HERE...
I KNOW, ALEX...
alex@alexcartoon.com

IF I MAKE IT AND YOU DON'T, IS THERE ANY MESSAGE YOU'D LIKE ME TO TAKE BACK? I MEAN, ARE YOUR FINANCIAL AFFAIRS IN ORDER? HAVE YOU MADE THE NECESSARY PROVISIONS?

YOU WOULDN'T WANT THERE TO BE AN UNDIGNIFIED SQUABBLE OVER THE DIVISION OF YOUR ASSETS?
MY WILL IS FULLY UP TO DATE... MY FAMILY WILL BE FINE...

ACTUALLY I WAS THINKING OF THE DEPARTMENTAL BONUS POOL. ...NOW, COULD I REMIND YOU OF MY ACHIEVEMENTS LAST YEAR?
DO WE HAVE TO START THIS AGAIN...?

Alex
PEATTIE + TAYLOR
WE'RE TRAPPED HERE IN THIS CREVASSE, ALEX. RESCUE HOPES ARE FADING AND IT'S GETTING COLD...
alex@alexcartoon.com

THIS COULD BE WHERE IT ALL ENDS FOR YOU AND ME... SO, TELL ME, ALEX: DO YOU BELIEVE IN GOD... THE AFTERLIFE? DO YOU THINK THERE'S A PLACE WE ALL GO WHEN WE DIE?
I DON'T KNOW, CYRUS...

BUT OBVIOUSLY IT'S A MATTER I'M GIVING SOME SERIOUS THOUGHT TO AT THIS PARTICULAR MOMENT IN TIME...

YOU'LL NEVER SEE HIM AGAIN SO, GO ON: TELL HIM WHAT YOU REALLY THINK OF HIM...
CITY WISDOM SAYS NEVER SLAG OFF YOUR BOSS. YOU'RE BOUND TO RUN INTO HIM AGAIN IN SOME NEW PLACE...
PROD
HMM...

Alex
PEATTIE + TAYLOR
THE SNOW'S FALLING HEAVILY. IT'S BELOW FREEZING... WE DON'T HAVE MUCH TIME, ALEX...
alex@alexcartoon.com

SURVIVAL IS OUR NUMBER ONE PRIORITY, BUT NEITHER OF US HAS ANY EXPERIENCE OF THIS SORT OF SITUATION... WE'VE GOT TO TAKE A DECISION ABOUT WHAT TO DO... AND QUICKLY...
I KNOW, CYRUS. BUT IT'S TOUGH.

IN TODAY'S TECHNOLOGICALLY ADVANCED SOCIETY ONE NEVER GIVES MUCH THOUGHT TO WHAT MIGHT HAPPEN IF ONE WERE TO FIND ONESELF STRANDED: ALONE, ISOLATED, MILES FROM CIVILISATION...
NO...

I GOOGLED "SNOW SURVIVAL" AND IT RETURNED 3,625,419 RESULTS.
WELL I'VE FOUND A WEBSITE WITH DIAGRAMS OF HOW TO BUILD AN IGLOO...
YES, BUT THIS OTHER WEBSITE ADVISES US TO DIG A SNOW TRENCH SHELTER...
HELL! BLASTED INFORMATION OVERLOAD...

Alex
PEATTIE + TAYLOR
IT'S GETTING COLD AND DARK, ALEX AND THERE'S STILL NO SIGN OF THE EMERGENCY SERVICES.
alex@alexcartoon.com

WE'RE STRANDED, ISOLATED AND ALONE WITH RESCUE HOPES FADING FAST. AN EXPERIENCE LIKE THIS GIVES ONE A VERY DIFFERENT PERSPECTIVE ON LIFE, DOESN'T IT?
YES INDEED.

THEY SAY THAT WHEN YOU KNOW YOU HAVEN'T GOT LONG TO LIVE, THE TINIEST, HUMDRUM, EVERYDAY THINGS SUDDENLY BECOME PROFOUNDLY FASCINATING AND SIGNIFICANT...

LIKE ALL THESE UTTERLY TEDIOUS INTERNAL OFFICE E-MAIL EXCHANGES THAT ONE GETS ROUTINELY COPIED IN ON?
YES. I'M FINDING THIS ONE BETWEEN THE PREMISES MANAGER AND THE HEAD OF I.T. UNUSUALLY INTERESTING...
YOU'RE LOSING IT, CYRUS..

Alex
PEATTIE + TAYLOR
SORRY TO INTERRUPT BUT THERE'S BEEN A SKIING ACCIDENT INVOLVING CYRUS AND ALEX...
WHAT?!
alex@alexcartoon.com

THEY'RE BOTH TRAPPED ON AN ISOLATED MOUNTAINSIDE... THE WEATHER'S DETERIORATING AND NIGHT IS CLOSING IN...
OH MY GOD... I HAD NO IDEA...

THE MOUNTAIN RESCUE SERVICE JUST CALLED TO SAY IT'S MAKING DESPERATE ATTEMPTS TO GET THROUGH TO THEM....
REALLY?
YES, BY PHONE...

SO COULD YOU ASK THEM BOTH TO GET OFF THE CONFERENCE CALL THEY'RE CURRENTLY ON WITH YOU...
CYRUS INSISTED WE TAKE IT
LISTEN, ALEX, THIS IS A CRUCIAL DEAL FOR THE BANK..

Alex
PEATTIE+TAYLOR
I THINK WE REACHED YOU JUST IN TIME, MY FRIEND. YOU HAVE A LITTLE HYPOTHERMIA BUT YOU'LL BE OK...

alex@alexcartoon.com
BUT I'M AFRAID YOUR COMPANION IS NOT IN SUCH A GOOD WAY... HE IS SUFFERING FROM CONCUSSION AND SEVERE HYPOTHERMIA...

HE IS SLIPPING IN AND OUT OF CONSCIOUSNESS... HE IS DELUSIONAL, RAMBLING. WHAT HE SAYS MAKES NO SENSE...
NO, NO... HE'S FINE...

HE REALLY DOES WANT YOU TO FLY HIM STRAIGHT TO HIS OFFICE...
ALEX, TELL THESE PEOPLE... I HAVE AN 11.00 MEETING...

Alex
PEATTIE+TAYLOR
I'M SURE YOU'LL ALL BE DELIGHTED TO HEAR THAT CYRUS AND ALEX HAVE BEEN SUCCESSFULLY RESCUED...

alex@alexcartoon.com
THEY'RE BEING FLOWN BACK BY AIR AMBULANCE. THEY'RE GOING TO BE FINE BUT THEY MAY NEED TO SPEND A COUPLE OF NIGHTS IN HOSPITAL AS A PRECAUTION...

OBVIOUSLY THE BANK WILL TAKE RESPONSIBILITY FOR ENSURING THEY RECEIVE THE APPROPRIATE MEDICAL CARE... THANK YOU...

ER... WHY ARE WE IN THIS NATIONAL HEALTH WARD, RUPERT?
SHH! WITH BONUS TIME COMING UP IT'S GOOD TO DAMP DOWN EXPECTATIONS BY SUGGESTING THE BANK IS HARD UP...

Alex
PEATTIE+TAYLOR
WE TAKE THE TRAIN TOGETHER EVERY MORNING, TONY, BUT THIS IS THE FIRST TIME I'VE SEEN YOU IN A SUIT...

alex@alexcartoon.com
WELL, AS YOU KNOW, ALEX, MANY BANKS THESE DAYS HAVE A DRESS-DOWN POLICY, BUT TODAY I HAVE A JOB INTERVIEW...
I SEE... BUT THE SWITCH IN ATTIRE MUST BE BOUND TO PROVOKE COMMENT...

YES, BUT OBVIOUSLY THERE ARE TIMES IN ONE'S PROFESSIONAL LIFE WHEN ONE TELLS THE TRUTH, AND OTHERS WHEN ONE AVAILS ONESELF OF A CONVENIENT LIE...
OF COURSE...

AND TODAY YOU CAN TELL THE TRUTH.
TO MY WIFE, YES... THAT I'VE GOT A JOB INTERVIEW...
AND YOU STILL HAVEN'T TOLD HER THAT YOU HAVEN'T ACTUALLY HAD A JOB SINCE YOU GOT FIRED SIX MONTHS AGO..?
WELL NO.

Alex
PEATTIE+TAYLOR
RUPERT, YOU SEEM A SOUND CHAP. WOULD YOU LIKE TO SIT ON MY COMPANY'S BOARD AS A NON-EXECUTIVE DIRECTOR?
I'D BE DELIGHTED TO, GAVIN...

alex@alexcartoon.com
HAVING A FEW INDEPENDENT DIRECTORS IS A REQUIREMENT THESE DAYS... IT'S JUST ANOTHER OF THESE TIRESOME RULES, DESIGNED TO STOP ME, AS CHIEF EXECUTIVE, RUNNING MY COMPANY AS I WANT...

IN THE SUPPOSED INTERESTS OF FAIRNESS AND ACCOUNTABILITY I FIND MYSELF HAVING TO EMPLOY SOME TOKEN IDIOT AT CONSIDERABLE EXPENSE TO PERFORM AN UTTERLY POINTLESS FUNCTION...
ER... AS NON-EXECUTIVE DIRECTOR?

NO, I'M TALKING ABOUT THE TAME HEADHUNTER I'M NOW GOING TO HAVE TO FORMALLY APPOINT TO DRAW UP A SHORTLIST WITH YOUR NAME AT THE TOP.
AH...

Alex
PEATTIE + TAYLOR
I'M DELIGHTED YOU'VE AGREED TO JOIN THE BOARD OF MY COMPANY AS NON-EXECUTIVE DIRECTOR, RUPERT...
SO AM I, GAVIN...

DID YOU HAVE ANY PARTICULAR ROLE IN MIND FOR ME?
WELL, I THOUGHT YOU COULD CHAIR OUR REMUNERATION COMMITEE... IT'S GOOD FOR THAT TO BE SEEN TO BE DONE BY A NEUTRAL PERSON...
alex@alexcartoon.com

EXECUTIVE PAY IS A THORNY ISSUE AND IT'S GENERALLY FELT THAT AN INDEPENDENT DIRECTOR WILL HAVE A PROPER IDEA OF COMPARATIVE SALARY SCALES...
BECAUSE OF OUR GENERAL BUSINESS BACKGROUND?

NO, BECAUSE IF YOU'RE POCKETING £40,000 FOR JUST TURNING UP TO A COUPLE OF LUNCHES A YEAR THEN THE SKY'S THE LIMIT AS TO WHAT THOSE OF US WHO DO THE REAL WORK SHOULD EARN...

Alex
PEATTIE + TAYLOR
HOW DID YOU FIND THAT BOARD MEETING RUPERT?
OH... A DODDLE... LIKE YOU, ALAN, I SIT ON A NUMBER OF BOARDS...
BOARD ROOM

OBVIOUSLY OUR ROLE AS NON-EXECUTIVE DIRECTORS IS TO GIVE THE EXECUTIVE DIRECTORS WHO ACTUALLY RUN THE COMPANY THE BENEFIT OF OUR GENERAL BUSINESS BACKGROUND AND EXPERTISE...
QUITE.
alex@alexcartoon.com

AND WHEN THE CHIEF EXECUTIVE SOUGHT OUT YOUR OPINION I THOUGHT YOU PROVIDED AN IMPRESSIVELY WIDE-RANGING, BIG-PICTURE, GENERIC, NON-INDUSTRY-SPECIFIC OVERVIEW...
THANK YOU...

ACTUALLY I'D DOZED OFF AND WHEN SOMEBODY NUDGED ME AWAKE I COULDN'T REMEMBER WHICH COMPANY I WAS AT...
THOSE BOARDROOMS... THEY ALL LOOK THE SAME, DON'T THEY?

Alex
PEATTIE + TAYLOR
OH LOOK... ISN'T THAT TREVOR LAWSON?
KEEP WALKING, CLIVE... I DON'T SPEAK TO HIM ANY MORE...

YOU'RE NOT STILL HARPING ON ABOUT THE TIME WHEN YOU AND HE WERE JOINT HEADS OF DERIVATIVES AT MEGABANK?
IT WAS OBVIOUS ONLY ONE OF US COULD SURVIVE... THERE WAS A BITTER POWER STRUGGLE...
alex@alexcartoon.com

COME ON, MIKE, YOU CAN'T KEEP BEARING A GRUDGE. THERE ARE WINNERS AND LOSERS IN ANY SITUATION... OKAY, SO YOU MISSED OUT ON THAT OCCASION, BUT LOOK ON THE BRIGHT SIDE...

AT LEAST YOU'RE STILL HEAD OF DERIVATIVES
YES, BUT HE GOT CANNED BY THE BANK, SET UP A HEDGE FUND AND NOW HE'S WORTH SQUILLIONS.
PAT

Alex
PEATTIE + TAYLOR
ALEX AND I HAVE BEEN MARRIED FOR A LONG TIME NOW AND OBVIOUSLY WE HAVE OUR UPS AND DOWNS...

BUT I SUPPOSE WITH THAT SPECIAL DATE IN THE CALENDAR COMING UP ANY WIFE CAN BE FORGIVEN FOR GETTING A BIT SENTIMENTAL ABOUT HER MARRIAGE...
FEBRUARY
alex@alexcartoon.com

IT'S THAT ONE DAY IN THE YEAR WHEN I LIKE TO THINK THAT WE CELEBRATE OUR TOGETHERNESS AND LOOK FORWARD CONTENTEDLY TO MANY MORE SUCH HAPPY OCCASIONS IN THE FUTURE...
SIGH YES... I KNOW WHAT YOU'RE TALKING ABOUT...

BONUS DAY... SO HOW MUCH DO YOU THINK ALEX WILL GET THIS YEAR?
HOPEFULLY ENOUGH FOR ME TO FORGIVE HIM WHEN HE FORGETS VALENTINE'S DAY AS USUAL...

Alex
PEATTIE + TAYLOR
I DON'T GET WHY WE HAVE TO DO AN ETHICS TEST THESE DAYS...
WE'RE INVESTMENT BANKERS... SURELY OUR JOB IS JUST TO MAKE MONEY?
ONLINE ETHICS TEST
ONLINE ETHICS TEST
alex@alexcartoon.com

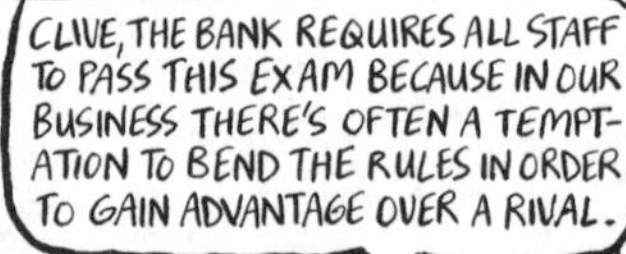
CLIVE, THE BANK REQUIRES ALL STAFF TO PASS THIS EXAM BECAUSE IN OUR BUSINESS THERE'S OFTEN A TEMPTATION TO BEND THE RULES IN ORDER TO GAIN ADVANTAGE OVER A RIVAL.

THE EXAM SETS OUT OUR EMPLOYER'S STANCE ON SUCH ISSUES. AFTER ALL ETHICS IS ABOUT TREATING OTHERS WITH INTEGRITY, RESPECT AND CONSIDERATION... SHOWING THEM LOYALTY AND COMPASSION...
RIGHT...

IN OTHER WORDS: THE EXACT OPPOSITE OF HOW THE BANK WOULD TREAT US?
THEY'D DROP US LIKE HOT BRICKS IF WE GOT IN TROUBLE... AND THEY'LL BE COVERED BECAUSE THEY GAVE US THIS "TRAINING"...
ONLINE ETHICS TEST
ONLINE ETHICS TEST

Alex
PEATTIE + TAYLOR
IT'S RIDICULOUS WE HAVE TO DO THIS 2-HOUR ETHICS TEST.
WE NEVER BOTHERED WITH STUFF LIKE THIS WHEN I STARTED IN THE CITY...
ONLINE ETHICS TEST
alex@alexcartoon.com

MAYBE, ALEX, BUT FOR MY GENERATION THE WORLD IS DIFFERENT. AS BANKERS WE NEED TO BE AWARE OF THE CONSEQUENCES OF OUR ACTIONS AND HOW THEY MAY AFFECT THE PEOPLE AROUND US...
ONLINE ETHICS TEST

WE HAVE TO THINK IN A MORE RESPONSIBLE WAY, ALEX. SOMETIMES WE NEED TO PUT OURSELVES IN THE PLACE OF OTHERS...
TRUE ENOUGH, CHRISTIAN

SUCH AS RIGHT NOW, WHEN YOU'RE GOING TO BE PUTTING YOURSELF HERE IN MY PLACE AND DOING THE EXAM FOR ME...
ONLINE ETHICS TEST
MAKE SURE IT'S FINISHED BY THE TIME I GET BACK FROM LUNCH.

Alex
PEATTIE + TAYLOR
SO, CHRISTIAN, HOW DID I DO IN MY ONLINE ETHICS EXAM?
YOU GOT 78%, ALEX. I HAVE PRINTED OUT YOUR CERTIFICATE...
ONLINE ETHICS EXAM
alex@alexcartoon.com

AH... WELL DONE ME... I MEAN, YOU...
BUT I DO NOT THINK IT WAS VERY ETHICAL OF YOU TO MAKE ME SIT AT YOUR DESK AND DO THE TEST FOR YOU WHILE YOU WENT TO LUNCH...
ONLINE ETHICS EXAM

DO YOU THINK ANY OF THE OTHER PEOPLE IN THIS DEPARTMENT HAVE SUCH LOW ETHICAL STANDARDS AS THIS, ALEX?
THAT'S NOT FOR ME TO SAY, CHRISTIAN...

IT'S FOR YOU... AFTER ALL, YOU'RE GOING TO BE TAKING ALL THEIR TESTS FOR THEM...
OH CHRISTIAN, I'LL NEED YOU TO DO MY ETHICS EXAM FOR ME TOMORROW LUNCHTIME...
AND MINE ON MONDAY...

Alex
PEATTIE + TAYLOR
CHRISTIAN, YOU'RE NOT STILL GRUMBLING BECAUSE A FEW OF US DELEGATED OUR ONLINE ETHICS TEST TO YOU...?
alex@alexcartoon.com

ALL OF YOU DID... I'VE SPENT EVERY LUNCHTIME THIS WEEK SITTING AT SOMEONE ELSE'S DESK DOING THEIR EXAM FOR THEM... IS THIS ETHICAL BEHAVIOUR BY YOU...? DO YOU REALISE WHAT IT DOES TO ME...?

I AM GETTING VERY JADED WITH THIS... EACH TIME ONE OF YOU FORCES ME TO DO THIS TEST I GET A LITTLE MORE CYNICAL AND DISILLUSIONED...

WELL, THAT'S GOOD. WE NEED THERE TO BE SOME VARIATION IN OUR SCORES.
AGREED. IT'D LOOK SUSPICIOUS IF WE ALL GOT THE SAME MARK.

Alex
PEATTIE + TAYLOR
I'VE SPENT EVERY LUNCH BREAK FOR THE LAST 3 WEEKS DOING THE ONLINE ETHICS TESTS FOR EVERYONE IN THE DEPARTMENT...

YOU HAVE ALL SCORED HIGH POINTS. YOU ARE ALL VERY "ETHICAL" PEOPLE...
THANK YOU, CHRISTIAN... AND AS SUCH WE'D LIKE TO SHOW OUR GRATITUDE BY BUYING YOU LUNCH...
alex@alexcartoon.com

OH... BUT DON'T FORGET TO DO YOUR OWN ETHICS TEST FIRST...
PAH! THIS WILL NOT TAKE LONG... I COULD DO IT WITH MY EYES CLOSED NOW...
ONLINE ETHICS EXAM

WELL... ALL THE ETHICS EXAM RESULTS ARE IN... THE ONLY SUSPICIOUS ONE IS A TRAINEE CALLED CHRISTIAN... HE ONLY TOOK 7 MINUTES TO COMPLETE THE 2 HOUR TEST.
HMM... HE MUST HAVE CHEATED. WE'LL HAVE TO DISCIPLINE HIM...
HUMAN RESOURCES

Alex
PEATTIE + TAYLOR
I CAN'T BELIEVE YOU STILL READ AN OLD-FASHIONED NEWSPAPER, ALEX...
THE BUGLE
alex@alexcartoon.com

THESE DAYS I UPLOAD THE NEWS CONTENT I REQUIRE DIGITALLY FROM THE INTERNET TO MY HANDHELD...
THE BUGLE
I FIND MY NEWSPAPER MORE PRACTICAL, CLIVE...

PRACTICAL...? LOOK AT THE SIZE OF IT... AND WE TAKE A TRAIN INTO TOWN EACH MORNING THAT'S JAM-PACKED WITH OTHER CITY COMMUTERS...
THE BUGLE
EXACTLY.

LOOK OUT! HERE COMES THAT UTTER BORE NIGEL COOTS...
OH CRIPES... NO...
THE BUGLE

CLIVE! I THOUGHT IT WAS YOU... SHALL WE SHARE A CARRIAGE?
OH, HELLO, NIGEL... ER... YES THAT WOULD BE DELIGHTFUL...
HOPELESSLY EXPOSED
DEEP COVER
THE BUGLE

Alex
PEATTIE + TAYLOR
WHAT DID YOU THINK OF PETER HAIN'S REMARKS THAT WE SHOULD GIVE 2/3 OF OUR BONUSES TO POOR PEOPLE?
IRRITATING.
BUSINESS CITY BONUS ROW
alex@alexcartoon.com

OF COURSE THE NEWSPAPERS LOVED IT BECAUSE IT GAVE THEM AN EXCUSE TO GET ON THEIR HOBBY HORSE ABOUT EXCESSIVE CITY PAY AGAIN...
IT'S TOTALLY IRRESPONSIBLE...

IT MERELY EXACERBATES TENSIONS THAT ALREADY EXIST... CREATING DIVISIONS BETWEEN US THE WEALTH CREATORS AND THOSE WHO THINK THEY'RE ENTITLED TO A BIG HAND-OUT JUST BECAUSE THEY'RE NEEDY...
THAT'S TRUE.

...BUT IT'S NOT A NICE WAY TO TALK ABOUT ONE'S WIFE.
SHE READS ALL THIS STUFF IN THE PAPER ABOUT BIG BONUSES AND STARTS GETTING ALL PARANOID AND SUSPICIOUS...
BUSINESS CITY BONUS ROW
SO FAR MINE'S HAD NO IDEA HOW MUCH I'M SECRETLY STASHING AWAY...

Alex
PEATTIE + TAYLOR
I'M AFRAID I'VE NEVER BEEN A GREAT BELIEVER IN EGALITARIANISM, CYRUS...
alex@alexcartoon.com

IT MIGHT APPEAL TO OTHER PEOPLE'S SENSIBILITIES TO HOLD THAT INDIVIDUALS SHOULD ALL BE TREATED EXACTLY THE SAME, BUT NOT MINE...

THERE WILL ALWAYS BE DIVISIONS AND DIFFERENTIALS WITHIN SOCIETY AND AS INVESTMENT BANKERS IT'S RIDICULOUS FOR US TO PAY LIP SERVICE TO SOME MISPLACED NOTION OF UNIVERSAL EQUALITY...

SO THAT'S WHY YOU'RE REFUSING TO FLY THIS NEW AIRLINE THAT'S ALL BUSINESS CLASS?
YES.
WHAT'S THE FUN IN IT IF THERE ARE NO ECONOMY CLASS PASSENGERS FOR US TO LORD IT OVER?

GYM
PERSONAL TRAINER

Alex
PEATTIE + TAYLOR
I'VE OFTEN WORRIED THAT ALEX ISN'T REALLY A TEAM PLAYER BUT MAYBE I SHOULD REVISE MY OPINION...

IN THE FIRE DRILL THIS MORNING HE WAS THE ONLY MEMBER OF THE DEPARTMENT WHO SEEMED PROPERLY INFORMED AND PREPARED...

alex@alexcartoon.com

I THOUGHT IT WAS PARTICULARLY IMPRESSIVE THAT HE HAD OBVIOUSLY FAMILIARIZED HIMSELF WITH THE LAYOUT OF THE EVACUATION ROUTES AND THE LOCATION OF EMERGENCY EXITS FROM THE BUILDING...

WELL, I'VE ALWAYS FOUND THE FIRE ESCAPE HANDY FOR SLIPPING BACK IN UNOBSERVED AFTER A LONG LUNCH...
AND SO FOR THE DRILL YOU JUST HAD TO REVERSE YOUR HABITUAL ROUTE...?

Alex
PEATTIE + TAYLOR
I'M STILL NOT SURE ABOUT WHETHER TO GO FOR THE COSMETIC SURGERY OR NOT...
HARLEY STREET
COSMETIC SURGEON

ACTUALLY, MR MASTERLEY, MANY CITY BANKERS THESE DAYS ARE ELECTING TO SPEND THEIR BONUSES ON GETTING RID OF WRINKLES, BAGS UNDER THE EYES, SAGGING JOWLS ETC...

alex@alexcartoon.com

I'M SURE YOU ARE WELL AWARE THAT IN THE BUSINESS WORLD ONE'S LOOKS CAN PLAY A SIGNIFICANT PART IN BOOSTING ONE'S EARNING POTENTIAL.
MOST DEFINITELY...

I PROBABLY ONLY GOT SUCH A LARGE BONUS OFF MY BOSS AS A RESULT OF LOOKING SO UTTERLY KNACKERED FROM EVIDENT OVERWORK...
SO, AS YOU SEE: THE SURGERY'S ALREADY PAID FOR...

Alex
PEATTIE + TAYLOR
COSMETIC SURGERY IS SOMETHING A LOT OF BANKERS CONSIDER WHEN THEY GET THEIR BONUS CHEQUES THESE DAYS, MR MASTERLEY.
HARLEY STREET W1

AFTER ALL THE MODERN CITY IS A YOUNG MAN'S GAME AND HAVING A FACE-LIFT CAN CONFER EVIDENT BUSINESS ADVANTAGES...
YES, I CAN SEE THAT...
alex@alexcartoon.com

THE PROCEDURE ITSELF IS SHORT AND STRAIGHTFORWARD. THE ONLY DOWNSIDE IS THAT YOU WILL NEED TO TAKE A FEW DAYS OFF WORK TO RECUPERATE FROM THE SURGERY...
EVEN BETTER.

MY BOSS WILL BE CONVINCED THAT I'M OFF SEEING HEADHUNTERS AND GET PARANOID THAT HE DIDN'T GIVE ME A BIG ENOUGH BONUS

Alex
PEATTIE + TAYLOR
A LOT OF CITY GUYS THESE DAYS FREELY ADMIT TO SPENDING THE PROCEEDS OF THEIR BONUSES ON COSMETIC SURGERY...
THEY DO?

OH YES. THE WORLD'S MOVED ON. IT'S NO LONGER AN ISSUE THAT HAS TO REMAIN SHROUDED IN SECRECY. IT'S NOT STIGMATISED IN SOCIETY AS IT USED TO BE.
REALLY?
alex@alexcartoon.com

FRANKLY IT'S SOMETHING MEN FEEL ABLE TO BE QUITE OPEN ABOUT THESE DAYS, TO TALK ABOUT IN DETAIL, EVEN COMPARE RESULTS WITH OTHER MEN...
YOU ARE JOKING?

I MEAN I DON'T EVEN TELL MY WIFE THE AMOUNT I GET...
I'M TALKING ABOUT PLASTIC SURGERY, NOT BONUSES...

Alex
PEATTIE+TAYLOR
IT'S FUNNY THE THINGS WE FIND OURSELVES DOING AS WE GET OLDER...

I MEAN, HERE I AM BOOKED INTO A HARLEY STREET CLINIC TO HAVE A FACE LIFT... I CAN JUST IMAGINE THE HORRIFIED REACTION OF MY 25-YEAR-OLD SELF...
alex@alexcartoon.com

AFTER ALL, BACK THEN IT WOULD HAVE SEEMED UTTER ANATHEMA TO ME TO BE EVEN CONTEMPLATING WHAT I AM SHORTLY ABOUT TO DO...
HAVE COSMETIC SURGERY?

NO. WALK OUT OF THIS VASTLY EXPENSIVE PRIVATE CLINIC WITH MY FACE OBSCURED BY BANDAGES AND HAVE NO ONE KNOW IT'S ME...

Alex
PEATTIE+TAYLOR
WHAT'S THAT, ALEX...? YOU'VE HAD COSMETIC SURGERY...? I DON'T BELIEVE MY EARS...

ONE'S GOT TO KEEP UP WITH THE YOUNGER GENERATION, DAD, AND TAKING CARE OF ONE'S BODY AND LOOKING GOOD IS IMPORTANT TO THAT...
I DON'T KNOW WHAT THE WORLD'S COMING TO...
alex@alexcartoon.com

IN MY DAY MEN WERE MEN... WE DIDN'T USE MOISTURISERS AND PONCE AROUND IN THE GYM: WE TOOK PART IN PROPER MANLY ACTIVITIES LIKE ROWING, RUGGER AND BOXING...

HEY, WHAT'S THAT BRUISING AROUND YOUR EYES, ALEX?
THAT...? OH I'VE TAKEN UP BOXING...
BOXING...? BO-TOXING MORE LIKE...

Alex
PEATTIE+TAYLOR
ALL RIGHT, CLIVE... I ADMIT IT. I'VE HAD COSMETIC SURGERY.

BUT NOW THAT YOU KNOW, WOULD YOU KINDLY KEEP IT A SECRET... IT'S NOT THE SORT OF THING A GENTLEMAN LIKES TO CONFESS TO.
alex@alexcartoon.com

SO FAR I'VE MANAGED TO AVOID ANYONE AT THE BANK ASKING ME TOO MANY DIRECT QUESTIONS AND ACTUALLY FINDING OUT THE TRUTH, BUT I'VE HAD A COUPLE OF CLOSE SHAVES...
YES...

...FROM YOUR JERMYN STREET BARBER... HE'S THE PERSON WHO TOLD ME...
ONE OF THE ANNOYING AFTER EFFECTS OF A FACE-LIFT IS THAT YOU GROW STUBBLE BEHIND YOUR EARS...

Alex
PEATTIE+TAYLOR
ALEX, WE CAN ALL SEE YOU'VE HAD COSMETIC WORK DONE, AND I JUST WANT TO SAY IT MAKES YOU LOOK TEN YEARS YOUNGER.

WHY, THANK YOU, TRICIA...
THERE YOU GO... OTHER PEOPLE TOLD ME I SHOULDN'T SAY ANYTHING TO YOU, BUT YOU'RE OBVIOUSLY PLEASED THAT I MENTIONED IT...
alex@alexcartoon.com

OF COURSE I AM... AFTER ALL, YOU WOMEN HAVE BEEN AVAILING YOURSELVES OF SUCH TECHNIQUES TO ENHANCE YOUR EARNING POTENTIAL FOR YEARS. WHY SHOULDN'T WE MEN DO THE SAME?
WHAT? HAVE PLASTIC SURGERY?

NO: CYNICALLY EXPLOIT POLITICALLY CORRECT LEGISLATION TO SUE THE BANK. NOW I BELIEVE YOUR COMMENT DRAWING ATTENTION TO MY AGE CONSTITUTES AN OFFENCE UNDER E.U. LAW...
ANTI-AGEISM DIRECTIVE

Alex
PEATTIE + TAYLOR
AS A LIFELONG NON-SMOKER, I FOR ONE WELCOME THE FORTHCOMING BAN ON SMOKING IN PUBS AND BARS IN THIS COUNTRY...

IF I WANT TO HAVE A SOCIAL DRINK WHY SHOULD I BE OBLIGED TO DO SO IN A FUG OF OTHER PEOPLE'S SMOKE AND HAVE THE STINK OF IT IMPREGNATING MY HAIR AND CLOTHES FOR HOURS AFTERWARDS..?

alex@alexcartoon.com

FRANKLY THIS NEW LEGISLATION SHOULD ALLOW NON-SMOKERS LIKE MYSELF TO REGAIN A FUNDAMENTAL HUMAN RIGHT...

THE RIGHT TO STOP OFF FOR A DRINK ON THE WAY HOME FROM WORK WITHOUT ONE'S WIFE FINDING OUT ABOUT IT?
QUITE. IN FUTURE I'LL JUST NEED MY TRUSTY BREATH FRESHENER...
CROWN AND ANCHOR
REEK
SQUIRT
PUB

Alex
PEATTIE + TAYLOR
I SEE YOU'VE GOT PEOPLE HERE FROM ALL THE MAJOR BANKS FOR TONIGHT'S WINE TASTING AND AUCTION, NEIL...

alex@alexcartoon.com
WE'VE ALL JUST BANKED OUR BONUSES AFTER A GOOD YEAR AND WE'RE INHERENTLY DEEPLY COMPETITIVE WITH EACH OTHER, SO THIS IS BOUND TO INFLUENCE HOW MUCH MONEY WILL BE RAISED FOR THE CHARITY...
I HOPE SO...

AND ALL THE AUCTION LOTS ARE TOP-OF-THE-RANGE AND DESIGNED TO APPEAL TO YOU CITY TYPES... A WEEKEND ABOARD A LUXURY SUNSEEKER MOTOR YACHT, FOR EXAMPLE... I IMAGINE WE'LL SEE YOU BIDDING FOR THAT, ALEX...

WHAT, AND ADMIT MY BONUS WASN'T BIG ENOUGH SIMPLY TO BUY A YACHT OUTRIGHT? NO FEAR...
ME NEITHER. I'M KEEPING MY HAND DOWN ALL EVENING...

Alex
PEATTIE + TAYLOR
I HEAR MALCOLM WAYHAM - GOOD TURNS 50 TOMORROW...
YES. AND HE'S BACK WORKING IN THE CITY AFTER A 5-YEAR ABSENCE...

alex@alexcartoon.com
PEOPLE HAVE QUESTIONED HOW EASY IT MIGHT BE FOR HIM TO RE-ADAPT AFTER SO LONG OUT OF THE MARKET. AFTER ALL, OURS IS A PEOPLE BUSINESS AND MEMORIES ARE SHORT...

OBVIOUSLY MALCOLM'S FIRST PRIORITY HAS BEEN TO GET OUT THERE AND RE-ESTABLISH HIS KEY RELATIONSHIPS, RE-INTRODUCE HIMSELF, PRESS THE FLESH, PUT IN "FACE TIME" WITH THE IMPORTANT PEOPLE...
RIGHT.

SO HE'S MANAGED TO REACQUAINT HIMSELF WITH EVERY MAITRE D' IN THE SQUARE MILE?
YES...
I SUPPOSE HE'D NOW BETTER GET AROUND TO TALKING TO SOME CLIENTS...
AH. GENNARO!

Alex
PEATTIE + TAYLOR
THESE GOVERNMENT MINISTERS WHO ATTACK THE COMPLACENCY OF THE CITY OF LONDON SHOW LITTLE UNDERSTANDING OF OUR WORLD...

alex@alexcartoon.com
WHAT PETER HAIN AND HIS SOCIALIST CRONIES WHO WANT TO TAKE AWAY OUR BONUSES SEEM TO FORGET IS THAT WE WORK VERY HARD FOR OUR MONEY...
THAT'S RIGHT.

AT A TIME LIKE THIS WHEN OUR BONUSES HAVE JUST BEEN PAID OUT WE IMMEDIATELY GET DOWN TO SETTING OUT OUR KEY OBJECTIVES FOR THE FORTHCOMING YEAR.
YES.

MY KEY OBJECTIVE IS TO TRY TO GET MYSELF MADE REDUNDANT.
ME TOO... AND ACTUALLY GET TIME TO DRIVE THAT MERCEDES I BOUGHT WITH LAST YEAR'S BONUS.

BY HOPING ENGLAND GETS KNOCKED OUT OF THE CRICKET WORLD CUP QUICKLY?

QUITE. IT SAYS HERE IT COULD COST THE COUNTRY £200M IN LOST WORKING HOURS IF WE PROGRESS IN THE TOURNAMENT...

NEWS

Alex
PEATTIE+TAYLOR
SO, NOT ONLY HAVE YOU FOUND OUT THAT YOUR FRIEND JULIAN IS TO LOSE HIS JOB, BUT YOU'VE ALSO BEEN ASKED TO INTERVIEW FOR IT?
THAT'S RIGHT, PENNY...
alex@alexcartoon.com

IT'S A VERY DELICATE STATE OF AFFAIRS... YOU AND I ARE HAVING DINNER WITH HIM AND HIS WIFE NEXT WEEK SO I SHALL TAKE THE OPPORTUNITY TO HAVE A QUIET WORD WITH HIM...

AFTER ALL, PEOPLE NEED TO BE INFORMED IF THERE'S ABOUT TO BE A MAJOR CHANGE IN THEIR EMPLOYMENT SITUATION WHICH COULD IMPACT ON THEIR FINANCIAL CIRCUMSTANCES AND LIFESTYLE...

SO, JULIAN, YOUR BANK LETS YOU FLY BUSINESS CLASS ON ALL ROUTES? AND DO YOU GET A CAR PARKING SPACE..?
WHY ARE YOU SUDDENLY SO INTERESTED IN DETAILS OF MY JOB, ALEX?
JOT JOT

Alex
PEATTIE+TAYLOR
ALEX MASTERLEY? THANK YOU FOR COMING IN FOR INTERVIEW...
NOT AT ALL...
CONTINENT BANK
alex@alexcartoon.com

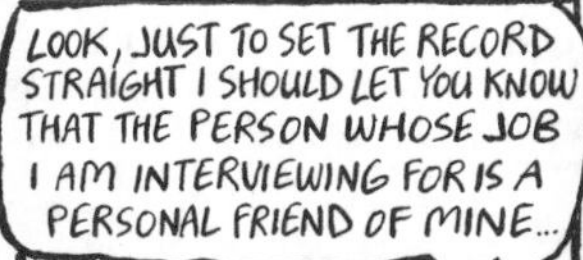

LOOK, JUST TO SET THE RECORD STRAIGHT I SHOULD LET YOU KNOW THAT THE PERSON WHOSE JOB I AM INTERVIEWING FOR IS A PERSONAL FRIEND OF MINE...
JULIAN CARTER? OH DEAR... THAT IS UNFORTUNATE...

I MEAN IT COULD HAVE BEEN HIGHLY EMBARRASSING IF YOU'D BUMPED INTO HIM IN THE BUILDING...
OH, THAT WAS UNLIKELY... BUT COULD WE GET A MOVE ON PLEASE...?

ANOTHER GLASS OF WINE WHILE YOU WAIT FOR YOUR COMPANION, MR CARTER?
BLOODY ALEX... HE ARRANGES TO MEET ME FOR LUNCH AND THEN STANDS ME UP... WHERE IS HE?

Alex
PEATTIE+TAYLOR
IT TURNS OUT THAT ONE OF THE CANDIDATES WE'RE INTERVIEWING FOR JULIAN CARTER'S JOB - ALEX MASTERLEY - IS A FRIEND OF HIS...
REALLY? THAT COULD BE TRICKY...
alex@alexcartoon.com

ALEX CLEVERLY ARRANGED TO HAVE LUNCH WITH JULIAN AND THEN CAME FOR INTERVIEW KNOWING THAT JULIAN WOULD BE WAITING IN THE RESTAURANT. ALEX LATER MADE SOME EXCUSE FOR STANDING HIM UP.

OH DEAR, OH DEAR... THIS IS ALL SO AWKWARD... AND EVEN IF WE DO FIND A REPLACEMENT FOR JULIAN WE'VE STILL GOT TO THINK UP SOME PRETEXT FOR SACKING HIM...
OH THAT'S SORTED...

"FALSIFYING AN EXPENSES CLAIM." LOOK, HE'S PUT "ALEX MASTERLEY" DOWN AS THE PERSON HE LUNCHED WITH...
AND ALEX WAS HERE WITH US THE WHOLE TIME...
SPLENDID!

Alex
PEATTIE+TAYLOR
THERE REALLY HAVE BEEN REMARKABLE CHANGES IN THE BUSINESS WORLD IN THE 20 YEARS WE'VE WORKED IN IT, ALEX...
alex@alexcartoon.com

JUST LOOK AT THE ADVANCES IN COMMUNICATION TECHNOLOGY. WE NOW HAVE PHONES THAT CAN SEND E-MAILS AND HAVE ACCESS TO THE INTERNET, BLOOMBERG AND OTHER INFORMATION SERVICES...

ESSENTIALLY THEY'RE A COMPLETE MOBILE OFFICE, ENABLING ONE TO DO ONE'S JOB WHEN ONE IS AWAY FROM ONE'S DESK...

...AND IN ONE OF THE COUNTLESS TEDIOUS SEMINARS AND MEETINGS WE'RE OBLIGED TO SIT THROUGH THESE DAYS...?
SIGH YES... IT ALL BALANCES OUT IN THE END...
TRANSPARENCY DIRECTIVE SEMINAR

Alex
PEATTIE + TAYLOR
HERE ARE YOUR SANDWICHES, GUYS...
THANKS HENRY... OH AND THERE'S A CALL FOR YOU ON LINE 3...
AH OKAY...

HELLO...? WHAT ARE YOU DOING CALLING ME ON THIS NUMBER? I THOUGHT YOU'D HAVE HAD SENSE ENOUGH TO PHONE ME ON MY MOBILE...
alex@alexcartoon.com

ESPECIALLY WHEN WE'VE HAD SENSITIVE DISCUSSIONS OF A FINANCIAL NATURE... I TRUST YOU HAVE NOT COMPROMISED MY POSITION BY DIVULGING ANY DETAILS TO MY COLLEAGUES...
WHAT?!
YOU MIGHT HAVE...?

SO I HAD A GOOD CHAT WITH HIS MUM AND SHE WAS SAYING HOW DELIGHTED HENRY WAS WITH HIS BONUS...
BUT HENRY, DEAR, £10,000 SEEMS A LOT OF MONEY TO ME...
TEE HEE...
I'LL NEVER LIVE THIS DOWN...

Alex
PEATTIE + TAYLOR
JULIAN, I THOUGHT YOU SHOULD KNOW THAT YOUR BANK HAS BEEN INTERVIEWING OTHER CANDIDATES FOR YOUR JOB...
WHAT?!

THEY'RE PLANNING TO FIRE ME? I DON'T BELIEVE IT...
I'M AFRAID IT'S TRUE AND IT JUST PROVIDES ANOTHER SORRY EXAMPLE OF HOW THE CALLOUS MODERN CITY WORKS...
alex@alexcartoon.com

THE HIGH-HANDED WAY THAT BANKS CASUALLY MAKE THESE ARBITRARY DECISIONS THAT CAN AFFECT A MAN'S WHOLE CAREER....
WELL, I APPRECIATE YOUR BEING SO SUPPORTIVE, ALEX...

ACTUALLY I'M TALKING ABOUT MY CAREER... THEY DIDN'T EVEN RECALL ME FOR A SECOND INTERVIEW... THE B*ST*RDS...

Alex
PEATTIE + TAYLOR
SO, ALEX, YOU'VE BEEN SECRETLY INTERVIEWING FOR MY JOB... YOU'RE SUPPOSED TO BE MY FRIEND!

DON'T YOU HAVE ANY CONCEPT OF PERSONAL INTEGRITY? OF LOYALTY TO YOUR MATES RATHER THAN TO YOUR JOB AND CAREER...?
ER...
alex@alexcartoon.com

MIGHT I REMIND YOU THAT I HAVE ALWAYS PUT MY OBLIGATIONS TO YOU AHEAD OF THOSE TO MY WORK. DOESN'T THAT MAKE YOU FEEL REMOTELY BAD, ALEX?
NOW THAT YOU MENTION IT, YES.

THAT INVITATION TO YOUR BANK'S BOX AT LORD'S THAT YOU SWING FOR ME IN LIEU OF A CLIENT... I SUPPOSE IT'LL GET RESCINDED ONCE THEY SACK YOU... DAMN...

Alex
PEATTIE + TAYLOR
MORE BOX TICKING HENRY...?
IT'S FOR OUR CLIENT RELATIONS MANAGEMENT TEAM. THEY WANT TO KNOW WHICH CLIENTS WE SPEAK TO AND HOW OFTEN...
TAP TAP
TAP TAP

I'M CLAIMING I SPEND ALL MY TIME TALKING TO THE BIG CLIENTS...
WINK
TAP
BUT AS A JUNIOR, SHOULDN'T YOU ADMIT YOU ONLY DEAL WITH THE SMALLER ONES?

NO WAY! EVERYONE CLAIMS THEY SPEAK TO THE BIG CLIENTS... I.E. THE ONES WHO GENERATE MONEY FOR THE BANK. AND THESE SURVEYS ARE USED TO DETERMINE HOW WE SHOULD BE REWARDED...
alex@alexcartoon.com

ACCORDING TO THIS SURVEY, CYRUS, ALL YOUR PEOPLE ARE TALKING TO THE SAME CLIENTS.
WE'D BETTER FIRE SOME OF THEM THEN. WE'LL START WITH THE MOST JUNIOR...
CLIENT RELATIONS MANAGEMENT
THAT'D BE HENRY...

Alex
PEATTIE + TAYLOR
UNDER CURRENT COMPLIANCE REGULATIONS ALL EMPLOYEES MUST TAKE AT LEAST ONE 2-WEEK HOLIDAY A YEAR...
COMPLIANCE DEPT.
alex@alexcartoon.com
THIS ENSURES THAT ANY ILLICIT DEALS THEY MIGHT BE DOING WOULD COME TO LIGHT IN THEIR ABSENCE...
BUT THAT WAS BEFORE PEOPLE HAD MODERN HANDHELDS...
EXACTLY. THOSE GADGETS ARE LIKE MOBILE OFFICES. SO WE MUST INSIST ALL STAFF TAKE A HOLIDAY WITHOUT THEIR BLACKBERRY, SO THEY'RE TOTALLY INCOMMUNICADO...
SO THEY WOULDN'T BE ABLE TO REPLY TO E-MAILS FROM MIDDLE OFFICE PEOPLE LIKE US...
AND NOTHING BAD WOULD HAPPEN AS A RESULT...
AND THEY'D REALISE WE'RE A TOTAL WASTE OF SPACE
AHEM..
I VOTE WE DROP THE WHOLE IDEA...

Alex
PEATTIE + TAYLOR
LOSING YOUR JOB MUST HAVE BEEN A REAL BLOW TO YOU, JULIAN...
WELL, YES, IT WAS, ALEX.
alex@alexcartoon.com
BUT ONE'S GOT TO LOOK ON THE POSITIVE SIDE... BEING UNEMPLOYED MEANS I CAN SPEND MORE TIME WITH MY SON JAKE, TAKE HIM TO SCHOOL, HELP HIM WITH EXTRA TUITION...
FOR EXAMPLE, WE WORK ON HIS ENGLISH EACH MORNING IN THE CAR... HE'S ONLY SIX BUT HE'S ALREADY GOT A VERY ADVANCED VOCABULARY FOR HIS AGE...
HOW COME YOUR DAD PICKS YOU UP FROM SCHOOL THESE DAYS, JAKE? HAS HE BEEN SACKED FROM HIS JOB?
NO, HE'S ON A SABBATICAL...
WHAT'S THAT?

Alex
PEATTIE + TAYLOR
THE NEWLY-APPOINTED M.D.S GET THEIR ROUND OF APPLAUSE AS THEY WALK BACK OUT ONTO THE FLOOR.
CLAP
CLAP
alex@alexcartoon.com
IT'S A EUPHORIC MOMENT IN ONE'S CAREER...
WHICH HOPEFULLY STOPS THEM REALISING THAT WE'VE JUST FOBBED THEM OFF WITH A NEW JOB TITLE IN LIEU OF A PAY RISE.
BUT IN THEIR NEW POSITIONS OF SENIORITY THEY'LL SOON LEARN TO APPRECIATE THAT COST-CUTTING IS AN ONGOING NECESSITY IN A MODERN INVESTMENT BANK.
SO WHEN DO WE ANNOUNCE THAT WE ARE WITHDRAWING FIRST CLASS TRAVEL PRIVILEGES FOR M.D.S?
GIVE IT A WEEK.. IT'S THE ONLY PERK THEY ACTUALLY GET...

Alex
PEATTIE + TAYLOR
REMEMBER, HENRY, THE FINANCIAL WORLD IS NOT AN ABSTRACTION. IT'S LINKED WITH THE REAL WORLD OF GOODS AND SERVICES...
alex@alexcartoon.com
WHEN CALLED UPON TO MAKE ECONOMIC JUDGEMENTS ONE NEEDS TO KNOW HOW TO READ A COMPANY BALANCE SHEET, BUT IT'S EQUALLY IMPORTANT TO USE ONE'S EYES AND COMMON SENSE.
FOR EXAMPLE, LOOK AROUND YOU. THIS RESTAURANT IS PACKED ON A MID-WEEK LUNCHTIME WITH CUSTOMERS OBVIOUSLY SPENDING LAVISHLY. WHAT CONCLUSIONS CAN YOU DRAW?
ER...
IT'S THE THOMSON-EXTEL SURVEY SEASON AND EVERYONE'S LUNCHING THEIR CLIENTS IN THE HOPE OF BUYING THEIR VOTE...?
QUITE.
IT'S GOT NOTHING TO DO WITH THE ECONOMY. THAT'S IN BIG TROUBLE.

Alex
PEATTIE + TAYLOR
THANKS TO YOU RICH CITY TYPES, ORDINARY PEOPLE LIKE ME CAN'T AFFORD TO BUY A HOUSE IN LONDON...
WHAT?

YOU LOT PUT YOUR OBSCENE BONUSES INTO PROPERTY AND PUSH THE MARKET OUT OF MY REACH...
LOOK, IT'S TRUE I EARN A LOT OF MONEY BUT LET ME TELL YOU: I WORK DAMNED HARD FOR IT...
alex@alexcartoon.com

MY BANK MAKES ME PUT IN LONG PUNISHING HOURS, I SPEND HALF MY LIFE TRAVELLING ON BUSINESS, I WORK EVENINGS, WEEKENDS, RIGHT THROUGH MY HOLIDAYS...

SO IT'S NOT MY FAULT IF MY SECOND WIFE HAS JUST FILED FOR DIVORCE... DO YOU THINK I WANT TO HAVE TO BUY ANOTHER HOUSE?
SEE? I TOLD YOU IT WAS THEM...

Alex
PEATTIE + TAYLOR
WELL, CLIVE, I'VE ARRANGED TO BUY MY SECRETARY LUNCH TODAY...
YES, CYRUS... SHE TOLD ME ABOUT IT... SHE'S VERY EXCITED...

THIS WAS A RESULT OF YOUR SUGGESTION THAT IN THIS COUNTRY IT'S NORMAL FOR A HEAD OF DEPARTMENT TO TREAT HIS P.A. TO LUNCH OCCASIONALLY
I HOPE YOU DIDN'T MIND ME MENTIONING IT.
alex@alexcartoon.com

NOT AT ALL, CLIVE. JUST BECAUSE I'M YOUR BOSS IT DOESN'T MEAN YOU CAN'T GIVE ME ADVICE...
WELL I'M GLAD YOU DIDN'T TAKE IT THE WRONG WAY...

HEY, BELINDA. HERE'S 20 QUID. GET YOURSELF WHATEVER YOU WANT AND I'LL HAVE A B.L.T. THANKS!
GLAMMED UP

Alex
PEATTIE + TAYLOR
EASTER IN THE CARIBBEAN, CLIVE... FOR ONCE YOU'VE COME GOOD WITH THE HOLIDAY ARRANGEMENTS...
THANK YOU, BRIDGET...
BARBADOS

THIS TIME I TOOK THE PRECAUTION OF SPEAKING TO THE HOTEL MANAGER IN PERSON... HE'S PROMISED US TWO WEEKS IN TROPICAL PARADISE...
BARBADOS
alex@alexcartoon.com

HE SAYS IT'S WARM EVERY DAY AND THE EVENINGS ARE BALMY. WE'LL LISTEN TO THE SOUND OF THE CRICKETS... I ASKED HIM TO PUT AN EXTRA FAN IN OUR ROOM...
FABULOUS.

YOU IDIOT, CLIVE.
OH ****!
AND THIS IS THE GENTLEMAN WHO'LL BE SHARING YOUR ROOM, SIR...
HOTEL RECEPTION
BURP
BARMY ARMY
ENGLAND CRICKET TEAM SUPPORT

Alex
PEATTIE + TAYLOR
STEWARDESS... THIS LADY YOU JUST PUT NEXT TO ME... IS SHE OKAY?
NO, I'M AFRAID SHE PASSED AWAY ON THE FLIGHT, SIR.

THERE WAS NO ROOM IN ECONOMY SO WE'RE PUTTING HER HERE IN FIRST CLASS.
WHAT? SHE'S DEAD? ARE YOU SURE? HAVE YOU DONE ALL THE TESTS?
alex@alexcartoon.com

YES, SIR... THERE'S NO SIGN OF A PULSE OR A HEARTBEAT OR BREATHING AND SHE'S QUITE COLD TO THE TOUCH...
WELL, IT'S GOOD TO MAKE SURE OF THESE THINGS...

YOU NEVER KNOW THE RUSES PEOPLE WILL STOOP TO JUST TO GET THEMSELVES A FREE UPGRADE...

Alex
PEATTIE + TAYLOR
I'M AFRAID THIS POOR LADY PASSED AWAY DURING THE FLIGHT, SIR...

YOU DIDN'T REALLY BELIEVE THAT SHE WAS SOMEHOW FAKING TO GET HERSELF AN UPGRADE TO FIRST CLASS?
AHEM... WELL, NO, NOT REALLY...
alex@alexcartoon.com

FRANKLY SHE'S BEEN LYING THERE STRETCHED OUT, INERT AND UTTERLY MOTIONLESS FOR THE LAST HOUR...
I HAD A PRETTY GOOD INKLING SHE WAS... YOU KNOW...
DEAD?

NO, A PROPER, LEGITIMATE FIRST CLASS PASSENGER... THOSE BLASTED UPGRADES CAN'T KEEP STILL FOR A MINUTE BECAUSE OF WANTING TO SAMPLE ALL THE FREE WINES, FOOD, MASSAGES ETC...

Alex
PEATTIE + TAYLOR
WHAT'S THE NEWS ON THE PASSENGER WHO DIED?
WE PUT HER IN THE FIRST CLASS CABIN... SHE'S BEING ATTENDED TO...

LUCKILY THERE WAS A DOCTOR IN BUSINESS CLASS... WE ALWAYS MAKE SURE WE ASCERTAIN SUCH PEOPLES' IDENTITIES WHEN THEY BOARD THE PLANE...
alex@alexcartoon.com

THAT AVOIDS US HAVING TO MAKE AN ANNOUNCEMENT OVER THE INTERCOM ASKING IF THERE'S A DOCTOR ON BOARD... AFTER ALL WE WOULDN'T WANT TO CREATE A PANIC...

I'M NOT REALLY A DOCTOR... I JUST PUT THAT ON MY PASSPORT SO I'LL GET UPGRADED...
SHOULDN'T YOU BE CHECKING FOR A PULSE IN THE NECK?
PANIC PANIC

Alex
PEATTIE + TAYLOR
I'M AFRAID THIS LADY'S DEAD. THERE'S NOTHING MORE I CAN DO... I'D BEST GET BACK TO MY SEAT...
WELL, THANKS FOR COMING IN, DOCTOR...

IT'S IRONIC REALLY, ISN'T IT? THIS POOR WOMAN'S LAID OUT HERE IN THIS FIRST CLASS CABIN BUT IT MEANS NOTHING TO HER ANY MORE... THERE'S A LESSON FOR US IN THIS...
alex@alexcartoon.com

YOU CAN BE SURROUNDED BY ALL THE TRAPPINGS OF LUXURY AND WEALTH BUT WHEN YOUR TIME COMES TO GO, YOU CAN'T TAKE IT WITH YOU, CAN YOU?
YOU CERTAINLY CAN'T...

SO HAND BACK THAT FIRST CLASS SPONGE BAG YOU'RE TRYING TO SLIP OFF WITH...
HE'S NOT EVEN A REAL DOCTOR ANYWAY...

Alex
PEATTIE + TAYLOR
WHAT'S GOING ON? MY CLIENT AND I ARE EN ROUTE TO THE CARIBBEAN TO WATCH THE CRICKET...

NOW WE'RE TOLD THAT THE PLANE IS BEING DIVERTED TO MIAMI...
WELL, SIR, YOU'RE AWARE OF THE PROBLEM WE HAVE WITH A CERTAIN PASSENGER ON BOARD...
alex@alexcartoon.com

IT'S JUST GOING TO BE A VERY BRIEF STOPOVER. JUST TO GIVE LOCAL OFFICIALS THE CHANCE TO REMOVE THE PERSON IN QUESTION FROM THE PLANE...
AARGH!
DON'T SAY THAT...

MY CLIENT IS THE C.E.O. OF AN INTERNET GAMING COMPANY. HE'S PARANOID ABOUT SETTING FOOT IN THE U.S.A....
I DEMAND A PARACHUTE...

ALEX WENT TO THE CARIBBEAN FOR THE CRICKET...

Alex
PEATTIE + TAYLOR
SO OUR BANK IS THE TARGET OF A TAKE-OVER BID?
YES... DUE TO OUR RECENT HISTORY OF UNDER-ACHIEVEMENT...

OF COURSE CERTAIN DEPARTMENTS WILL BE SAFE - THOSE IN AREAS WHERE THE BIDDING BANK DOESN'T HAVE A PRESENCE - BUT IN OTHERS THERE WILL BE NECESSARY REDUNDANCIES...

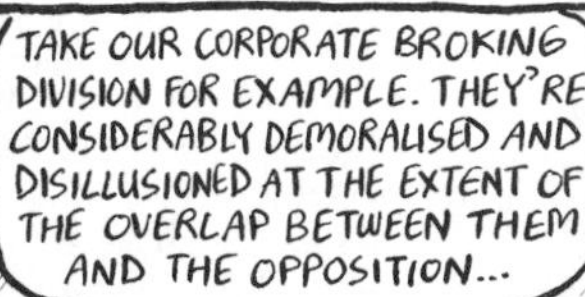
TAKE OUR CORPORATE BROKING DIVISION FOR EXAMPLE. THEY'RE CONSIDERABLY DEMORALISED AND DISILLUSIONED AT THE EXTENT OF THE OVERLAP BETWEEN THEM AND THE OPPOSITION...

NONE WHAT-SOEVER?
EXACTLY, WHICH MEANS THEY'LL MISS OUT ON THE BIG REDUNDANCY CHEQUES THAT'LL BE FLYING AROUND...
MMM... MAYBE THIS IS THE ROOT OF OUR PROBLEM...

Alex
PEATTIE + TAYLOR
OUR BANK IS THE SUBJECT OF TAKEOVER SPECULATION AND IT NOW SEEMS THERE MAY BE MULTIPLE BIDDERS INVOLVED...
YES

THESE EVER-CHANGING RUMOURS ARE CAUSING ALL MANNER OF UNCERTAINTY AND INSTABILITY...
WELL AT LEAST IT'S CONCENTRATED THE ATTITUDES OF MY TEAM...

LOOK AT THE EFFECT ON ALEX. NORMALLY HE'D BE AT LUNCH, BUT HE'S BEEN GALVANISED INTO SITTING AT HIS DESK AND ACTUALLY DOING SOME WORK...

I'VE JUST DEVISED THIS SPREADSHEET THAT TRACKS THE MARKET AND CALCULATES THE VALUE OF MY MEGA-BANK SHARE OPTIONS AT ANY TIME...
NOW YOU JUST HAVE TO GET YOURSELF ON THE REDUNDANCY LIST SO YOU CAN CASH THEM IN...
MEGA BANK

Alex
PEATTIE + TAYLOR
ALEX, CAN YOU DO A CLIENT MEETING THIS AFTERNOON?
DON'T BE SILLY, CLIVE. OUR BANK IS THE SUBJECT OF A TAKEOVER BID.

AND IT'S JUST BEEN ANNOUNCED THAT "RETENTION BONUSES" WILL BE PAID TO KEY STAFF, SO I'M SPENDING ALL MY TIME SENDING E-MAILS TO EVERYONE INTERNALLY TO SHOW HOW IMPORTANT I AM...

BUT I'M ALSO BUSY SEEING HEAD-HUNTERS TO SET MYSELF UP WITH A NEW JOB.
ALEX, ALL THESE DEVIOUS AND SELF-INTERESTED SCAMS YOU'RE CONSTANTLY PERPETRATING... DON'T THEY EVER MAKE YOU FEEL BAD?
YES, OF COURSE...

AFTER THE TAKEOVER GOES THROUGH I'M GOING TO HAVE TO SHAM BEING USELESS TO GET MYSELF MADE RED-UNDANT...
SO YOU GET A RETENTION BONUS, A SEVERANCE PAYMENT AND THEN A SIGN-ON FEE SOMEWHERE NEW?
IT'S CALLED PASSING "GO" THREE TIMES.

Alex
PEATTIE + TAYLOR
HOW'S BUSINESS AT MEGABANK SINCE YOU BECAME THE TARGET OF A TAKEOVER BID, ALEX?
NON EXISTENT, CAROLYN.

EVERYONE'S TOO PREOCCUPIED WITH SAVING THEIR OWN SKINS TO DO ANY WORK AND OF COURSE NO CLIENTS WANT TO DEAL WITH AN ORGANIS-ATION THAT MIGHT NOT EXIST IN SIX MONTHS' TIME.

BUT I'M A CLIENT, ALEX, AND YOU'RE HAVING LUNCH WITH ME. THAT'S GOT TO BE GOOD, SURELY?
WELL, I MENTIONED TO MY BOSS THAT I WAS SEEING YOU TODAY...

HE'S CONVINCED I MUST HAVE A NEW JOB LINED UP AND I'M TRYING TO LURE YOU TO JOIN ME...
THE PARANOIA GETS TO EVERYONE, DOESN'T IT?
PERHAPS I SHOULD JUST ADMIT THAT WE'RE HAVING AN AFFAIR...

Alex
PEATTIE + TAYLOR
EVERYONE KNOWS THAT A BROKER'S DUTY IN SPRING IS TO BE OUT AT LUNCH EVERY DAY OF THE WEEK.
alex@alexcartoon.com

IT'S THE THOMSON-EXTEL SURVEY SEASON AND WE HAVE TO BUY OUR CLIENTS' VOTES BY PLYING THEM WITH FOOD AND DRINK... BUT TRY TELLING THAT TO THE MIDDLE-OFFICE BUSY-BODIES WHO RUN OUR LIVES...

THESE DAYS MY EXISTENCE FEELS LIKE A CONSTANT STRUGGLE AGAINST THE BOX-TICKERS WHO SEEM INTENT ON PREVENTING ME FROM DOING MY JOB...
I KNOW WHAT YOU MEAN...

IT'S A BAD TIME FOR THEM TO BE ASKING YOU TO DO YOUR ANNUAL MEDICAL...
I HAVEN'T A HOPE IN HELL OF PASSING RIGHT NOW...

Alex
PEATTIE + TAYLOR
THE MODERN BUSINESS WORLD IS A GLOBAL 24-HOURS-A-DAY OPERATION...
alex@alexcartoon.com

OUR CLIENTS EXPECT US TO BE ON DUTY ROUND THE CLOCK AND NOT JUST FOR THE 14 HOURS OR SO A DAY WE'RE AT OUR DESKS

HAVING BLACKBERRIES MEANS MY TEAM CAN RESPOND TO E-MAILS WHENEVER AND WHEREVER THEY ARE, WITH THE RESULTANT EFFECT ON BUSINESS EFFICIENCY...

OH NO!... I JUST REALISED I REPLIED TO A CLIENT'S E-MAIL LAST NIGHT WHEN I WAS DRUNK AND TOLD HIM EXACTLY WHAT I THOUGHT OF HIM...
THAT'S PROBABLY BLOWN THE DEAL... WHAT ARE YOU GOING TO TELL CYRUS?
DREAD

Alex
PEATTIE + TAYLOR
HENRY, HAVE YOU WRITTEN THE PRESENTATION FOR THE CAREERS TALK I'M GIVING AT MY SON'S SCHOOL TODAY?
YES, ALEX.

I'VE FOCUSED ON THE WAY THE BUSINESS WORLD HAS CHANGED IN YOUR TIME WITH THE RECENT REGULATORY MOVES TOWARDS GREATER TRANSPARENCY, FAIRNESS AND EQUALITY OF ACCESS TO INFORMATION...

alex@alexcartoon.com

I THINK IT WOULD IMPRESS THE STUDENTS IF YOU WERE TO FOLLOW THE LEAD OF OTHER IMPORTANT BUSINESS FIGURES IN DEMANDING A LEVEL PLAYING FIELD...
I ALREADY HAVE.

SO THIS IS WHY HE NEEDED THE LEVEL PLAYING FIELD...
IT'S CERTAINLY IMPRESSED THE BOYS.
WHIRR

Alex
PEATTIE + TAYLOR
NOW, WHEN I READ A GRADUATE'S C.V. WHAT I'M REALLY LOOKING FOR IS EVIDENCE OF CHARACTER AND INITIATIVE...
CAREERS TALK: BANKING

I'LL BE MUCH MORE IMPRESSED IF YOU'VE SPENT YOUR HOLIDAYS BUILDING A SCHOOL IN AFRICA OR RUNNING YOUR OWN INTERNET BUSINESS RATHER THAN JUST DOING SO-CALLED "WORK EXPERIENCE" IN SOME CITY OFFICE...
alex@alexcartoon.com

THIS IS WHERE THESE CAREER SEMINARS CAN BE PRODUCTIVE, ALLOWING USEFUL, PRACTICAL INFORMATION LIKE THIS TO BE PASSED FROM GENERATION TO GENERATION...

SO KINDLY TELL YOUR PARENTS NOT TO SUBJECT ME TO THE USUAL HARASSMENT AT SPORTS DAY TO GET YOU INTERNSHIPS AT MY BANK THIS YEAR...
THANK YOU... NOW, TO MOVE ON...

Alex
PEATTIE + TAYLOR
I HOPE I'VE GIVEN YOU SOME INSIGHT INTO WHAT IT WOULD BE LIKE TO WORK FOR AN INVESTMENT BANK.
CAREERS TALK

NOW, WHAT YOU ALL WANT TO KNOW IS: HOW MUCH WILL YOU EARN? ...I ALWAYS SAVE THIS BIT TILL THE END BECAUSE I ENJOY SEEING THE LOOKS ON YOUR FACES WHEN I REVEAL THE NEWS...
AGOG
alex@alexcartoon.com

THIS IS THE STARTING SALARY THAT MEGABANK CURRENTLY PAYS TO GRADUATES...
£42,000 PER ANNUM
!!!
BUT...

WITH THE HOURS YOU'LL BE PUTTING IN, YOU'D BE BETTER OFF CLEANING LAVATORIES FOR A LIVING...
15 HOURS A DAY
7 DAYS A WEEK
50 WEEKS A YEAR
=
£8 PER HOUR
HEH, HEH... YES, THAT'S MORE LIKE IT...

Alex
PEATTIE + TAYLOR
WELL, I THOUGHT THAT CAREERS TALK FROM CHRISTOPHER MASTERLEY'S DAD WAS VERY INFORMATIVE...
CAREER TALK
YES. ME TOO.
alex@alexcartoon.com

IT MUST BE HARD FOR A SENIOR PERSON LIKE HIM TO RELATE TO THE LIFE OF A JUNIOR EMPLOYEE, AND OBVIOUSLY THE BUSINESS WORLD HAS CHANGED A LOT SINCE HE FIRST STARTED IN IT...

BUT HIS TALK LEFT ME WITH A VERY CLEAR UNDERSTANDING OF WHAT I'D BE DOING IF I WAS A GRADUATE TRAINEE AT MEGABANK...

PROGRAMMING HIS POWERPOINT PRESENTATIONS FOR HIM?
WELL, FROM THE WAY HE PANICKED WHEN HE ACCIDENTALLY CLICKED OVER 2 SLIDES AT ONCE ONE CAN GUESS HE DIDN'T DO IT HIMSELF...
CAREER TALK

Alex
PEATTIE + TAYLOR
SO, ALEX, DID YOUR CAREERS TALK TO OUR SIXTH FORMERS GIVE YOU ANY IDEA WHICH OF THEM MIGHT BE CUT OUT FOR A CAREER IN THE CITY?
MASTERS' NOTICEBOARD
YES, HEADMASTER...
alex@alexcartoon.com

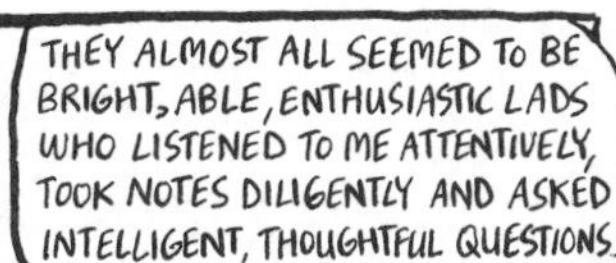
THEY ALMOST ALL SEEMED TO BE BRIGHT, ABLE, ENTHUSIASTIC LADS WHO LISTENED TO ME ATTENTIVELY, TOOK NOTES DILIGENTLY AND ASKED INTELLIGENT, THOUGHTFUL QUESTIONS.

THOUGH I'M AFRAID MY OWN SON CHRISTOPHER MERELY SAT AT THE BACK, PAID NO ATTENTION TO ANYTHING I WAS SAYING AND SPENT THE WHOLE TIME LOOKING AT HIS WATCH...
YES, DAD...

I WAS RUNNING A BOOK ON HOW LONG YOU'D SPEAK FOR... LOOK, I MADE £16...
RUFFLE
HA! YES! THAT'S MY BOY! YOU'VE GOT WHAT IT TAKES!
PRIDE

Alex
PEATTIE + TAYLOR
THANKS FOR TAKING THE TIME TO COME IN AND TALK TO THE BOYS, ALEX...
MY PLEASURE, HEADMASTER.

I THINK YOU'VE REALLY ENTHUSED THEM TO CONSIDER A CAREER IN THE CITY...
THAT'S GOOD, BUT I WASN'T ABLE TO DEMONSTRATE ALL THE QUALITIES IT TAKES TO BE AN INVESTMENT BANKER...
alex@alexcartoon.com

THE POWERS OF NEGOTIATION AND PERSUASION THAT ONE NEEDS TO POSSESS IN BUSINESS SITUATIONS WHERE ONE IS CALLED ON TO USE SHREWDNESS, INITIATIVE AND RESOURCEFULNESS...

SO, ALEX, HOW DO YOU PROPOSE TO JUSTIFY THIS HELICOPTER YOU'RE CLAIMING ON YOUR EXPENSES?
DEEP BREATH
OKAY, HERE GOES...

Alex
PEATTIE+TAYLOR
OVER THE YEARS THE BANK HAS TRADITIONALLY PAID OUT A PROPORTION OF STAFF BONUSES IN COMPANY STOCK.

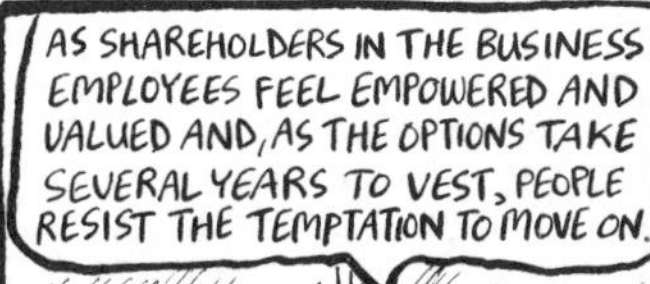
AS SHAREHOLDERS IN THE BUSINESS EMPLOYEES FEEL EMPOWERED AND VALUED AND, AS THE OPTIONS TAKE SEVERAL YEARS TO VEST, PEOPLE RESIST THE TEMPTATION TO MOVE ON.

THE ENSUING SPIRIT OF CORPORATE LOYALTY AND COMMITMENT TO THE COMPANY IS SOMETHING WE NEED TO BE ABLE TO COUNT ON IN TIMES OF CRISIS...
LIKE NOW, WHEN WE'RE FACING A TAKEOVER BID...

...AND EVERYONE'S DESPERATE TO GET MADE REDUNDANT BECAUSE IT WOULD PERMIT THEM TO CASH IN ALL THEIR SHARE OPTIONS?
HMM... PERHAPS THIS IS A POLICY WE NEED TO RETHINK...

Alex
PEATTIE+TAYLOR
WE'RE ALL VERY DISAPPOINTED IN YOU, ALEX...

WHAT YOU'VE DONE IS QUITE POSSIBLY ILLEGAL AND CERTAINLY CONTRARY TO THE CORPORATE SPIRIT WE AIM TO INSTIL IN MEGABANK EMPLOYEES...

THE BANK WAS VERY GENEROUS IN THE BONUSES IT PAID OUT TO STAFF IN MARCH, YET YOU CHOSE TO PERPETRATE AN ACT OF RANK DISLOYALTY AND BETRAY YOUR EMPLOYER LIKE THIS..

ER... BY BUYING SHARES IN THE BANK.
WELL, WHEN OUR BONUSES WEREN'T PAID IN COMPANY STOCK THIS YEAR I GUESSED YOU WERE HOPING TO GET SOMEONE ELSE TO GIVE YOU MORE FOR IT... IE: A TAKEOVER WAS IN THE OFFING...

Alex
PEATTIE+TAYLOR
WITH VARIOUS RIVAL BIDDERS IN THE OFFING, THIS TAKE-OVER BATTLE FOR THE BANK COULD DRAG ON FOR ANOTHER 6 MONTHS.

I REALISE HOW FRUSTRATING IT MUST BE FOR YOU AND YOUR TEAM BEING IN LIMBO LIKE THIS...
IT'S TRUE, RUPERT, BUT HAVE NO DOUBTS ABOUT OUR STEADFASTNESS...

THERE'S A GOOD CORPORATE SPIRIT ABOUT US WITH A STRONG UNDER-LYING FIBRE OF COMMITMENT AND RESOLVE... WE'RE IN THIS FOR THE LONG HAUL AND ARE DETERMINED TO SEE IT THROUGH...

SO THEY'RE ALL HANGING ON IN THERE IN CASE THERE'S A REDUNDANCY CHEQUE AT THE END OF IT FOR THEM?
SIGH, YES... I'D HOPED THE BOREDOM MIGHT HAVE PERSUADED SOME OF THEM TO JUMP SHIP EARLY.

Alex
PEATTIE+TAYLOR
OH BLAST, IT'S MY WIFE PHONING... I HOPE NOTHING'S WRONG.
GIRLIE BAR
FLASH
RING

HELLO, DARLING... EVERYTHING OK...? YOU KNOW IT'S THE MIDDLE OF THE NIGHT OVER HERE IN HONG KONG WHAT AM I DOING? OH, JUST HAVING A NIGHTCAP WITH A COUPLE OF COLLEAGUES...
Shh...
WINK

WHAT?!... DON'T BE SILLY, DARLING.. OF COURSE I'M NOT IN A LAPDANCING BAR! SPENDING A FORTUNE ON EXOTIC DANCERS? WHERE DO YOU GET THESE ABSURD IDEAS?

ER... FROM MY CREDIT CARD COMPANY? WHO JUST PHONED OUR HOME NUMBER TO REPORT A POSSIBLE FRAUDULENT USE IN THE "HANKY SPANKY" BAR IN HONG KONG...?

DO YOU HAVE ANOTHER CARD, SIR? THIS ONE HAS BEEN REFUSED...

AH... ER...

RIP

Alex
PEATTIE + TAYLOR
I'M SORRY, SIR... MR GEKKO'S NOT SEEING VISITORS TODAY...
BUT I'M BUD FOX...
ZZZ

WHO WAS THAT WHO JUST WENT INTO MR GEKKO'S OFFICE?
HE SAID HIS NAME WAS ALEX AND THAT HE'S A FAN...
GORDON GEKKO
BUT GORDON'S ON THE PHONE TO A CLIENT...
alex@alexcartoon.com

HOLD ON, BRAD... WE GOT A KIND OF BAD CONNECTION HERE... YEAH... THERE'S AN ECHO ON THE LINE... CAN YOU HEAR IT...?
ANYWAY... LIKE I WAS SAYING...

"LUNCH IS FOR WIMPS"...
HERO WORSHIP
GODDAM! THERE IT IS AGAIN...

Alex
PEATTIE + TAYLOR
SO YOU'RE FROM THE FUTURE, HUH?
THAT'S RIGHT, MR GEKKO, AND THE FINANCIAL WORLD HAS CHANGED A LOT...

AFTER THE EXCESSES OF THE 80'S THE AUTHORITIES FELT THE NEED TO CRACK DOWN... WE'RE TOTALLY HIDEBOUND BY REGULATIONS NOW...
alex@alexcartoon.com

I CAN TELL YOU, THE SORT OF PRACTICES YOU OPENLY INDULGE IN WOULD BE UTTERLY ILLEGAL IN MY TIME...
YEAH?

I MEAN, SMOKING IN YOUR OFFICE? UNHEARD OF...
INSIDER DEALING'S STILL RIFE THOUGH.
PUFF PUFF

Alex
PEATTIE + TAYLOR
SO IN YOUR FUTURE PEOPLE CAN'T SMOKE IN OFFICES, HUH?
WALL STREET
ZZZ
NO, MR GEKKO.

HEALTH AND SAFETY CONCERNS YOU SEE. EVEN YOUR FAVOURITE DISH STEAK TARTARE WOULD BE BANNED IN MOST RESTAURANTS IN MY TIME.
YOU'RE KIDDING.
I'M NOT.
alex@alexcartoon.com

HEALTH IS THE BIG THING. EVERYONE'S OBSESSED WITH GOING TO THE GYM... NOW, YOU'VE GOT MULTIPLE DEALS TO BE DOING, MR GEKKO... YOU'RE NOT GOING TO WASTE VALUABLE TIME PUMPING IRON, ARE YOU?
NO WAY! WHO NEEDS THAT?

BRAD, BUY ME 2 MILLION BLUE STAR AT 14 3/8...
MARV, SHORT TREASURY BONDS.
BULGE
BULGE
LIFT
LIFT

Alex
PEATTIE + TAYLOR
MR GEKKO TELLS ME YOU'RE FROM THE FUTURE, ALEX... IS THE FINANCIAL WORLD VERY DIFFERENT?
IT CERTAINLY IS, BUD...

REGULATION'S BEEN TIGHTENED UP HUGELY IN MY DAY... COMPLIANCE DEPARTMENTS IN BANKS NOW WIELD COLOSSAL POWER... A LOT OF THINGS HAVE CHANGED SINCE THESE TIMES...
alex@alexcartoon.com

I CAN TELL YOU: IF I WANTED TO ENGAGE IN A SPOT OF SHADY DEALING THERE'S NO DOUBT WHICH DECADE I'D RATHER LIVE IN...
RING
EXCUSE ME...

MY OWN... AT LEAST IT'S POSSIBLE TO BE DISCREET WHEN USING A MOBILE...
I SEE BUD'S DOING ANOTHER INSIDE TRADE...
BLUE HORSESHOE LOVES ANACOT STEEL...

Alex
PEATTIE+TAYLOR
IN MY DAY, MR GEKKO, MOBILE PHONES ARE SO COMMON THAT EVERYONE HAS ONE...
REALLY?
WALL ST.
WALL STREET
ZZZ

AND THEY DON'T JUST MAKE CALLS: THEY TAKE PHOTOS, PLAY MUSIC, SEND E-MAILS...
E-MAILS? WHAT'S THAT?
alex@alexcartoon.com

...IN FACT IN 2007 A NEW YORK SENATOR PROPOSED BANNING THEIR USE WHEN CROSSING THE STREET BECAUSE OF THE NUMBER OF ACCIDENTS BEING CAUSED...
WALK
YEAH...?
TAP TAP

HEY! SEE THAT FELLA? HE'S GOT ONE OF THEM NEW-FANGLED PORTABLE TELEPHONE THINGIES...
DON'T WALK
BEEP BEEP
TAXI
SCREECH

THUD
TAXI
I GUESS SOME THINGS NEVER CHANGE...

Alex
PEATTIE+TAYLOR
ALEX, ARE YOU PERSONALLY ACQUAINTED WITH EVERY MAITRE D' IN TOWN?
IT'S POSSIBLE.
MENU
FRANCO'S
alex@alexcartoon.com

I MEAN, WE WALK INTO THIS TOTALLY OBSCURE, OUT OF THE WAY RESTAURANT AND IMMEDIATELY IT'S "HELLO STEFANO" AND "GOOD AFTERNOON, MR MASTERLEY."
FRANCO'S

AND THEN, WITHIN 2 MINUTES OF US SITTING DOWN, A BOTTLE OF CHAMPAGNE ARRIVES AT OUR TABLE "WITH THE COMPLIMENTS OF STEFANO."
FRANCO'S

WHAT'S HE DOING HERE ANYWAY? HE WORKS AT "LE GOURMET."
HAVING A DISCREET LUNCH WITH THE PROPRIETOR OF A RIVAL RESTAURANT AND, JUDGING BY THIS BRIBE, HE'S SECRETLY INTERVIEWING FOR A JOB..
(SHH)
FRANCO'S

Alex
PEATTIE+TAYLOR
STEFANO, YOU'VE BEEN THE MAITRE D' AT LE GOURMET FOR 25 YEARS AND YOU'RE THE BEST IN TOWN...

SO I'LL DOUBLE YOUR SALARY IF YOU'LL COME AND WORK FOR MY RESTAURANT, JONES'S
THAT'S A VERY TEMPTING OFFER. WOULD I NEED TO DO AN INTERVIEW?
alex@alexcartoon.com

DON'T BE SILLY. YOU'RE A LEGEND. LOOK AT YOU... YOU DON'T EVEN WORK HERE BUT YOU'RE POSITIVELY TWITCHING AT THE SIGHT OF THAT DINER USING HIS MOBILE PHONE...
ER, YES... EXCUSE ME A MINUTE...

...ROGER, I WANT YOU TO LIQUIDATE MY ENTIRE SHAREHOLDING IN LE GOURMET RESTAURANT... LOOKS LIKE STEFANO'S OFF...
MR MASTERLEY, YOU PROMISED YOU WOULDN'T TELL ANYONE YOU SAW ME HERE...

Alex
PEATTIE+TAYLOR
I SUPPOSE YOUR SON WILL BE DOING WORK EXPERIENCE IN HIS HOLIDAYS...
WELL HE'S KEEN ON A CAREER IN THE CITY...

IN OUR DAY WE'D JUST DO SOME SUMMER BAR WORK TO EARN ENOUGH MONEY TO GO TRAVELLING, BUT THE BUSINESS WORLD HAS CHANGED AND KIDS THESE DAYS ARE MORE CLUED UP...
alex@alexcartoon.com

CHRISTOPHER WANTS TO GET PROPER HANDS-ON EXPERIENCE OF THE CITY, TO BE AT THE CUTTING EDGE OF WHERE THE DEALS ARE HAPPENING, TO GAIN INSIGHTS INTO HOW OUR BUSINESS WORKS...

SO HE'S GOT A JOB AT STARBUCKS ROUND THE CORNER...
WITH THE MODERN COMPLIANCE REGIME ITS THE ONLY PLACE PEOPLE DARE TALK BUSINESS THESE DAYS...
AND ANYTHING HE OVERHEARS, HE'LL REPORT STRAIGHT BACK TO ME. HEH HEH.

Alex
PEATTIE+TAYLOR
MY BANK ALLOWS EMPLOYEES TO TAKE A 3-MONTH SABBATICAL ON FULL PAY AFTER 10 YEARS' SERVICE. I'M THINKING OF DOING THAT NEXT YEAR...
alex@alexcartoon.com

IS THAT A GOOD IDEA, JEREMY? WILL IT SEND OUT THE RIGHT SIGNALS? MIGHT IT NOT IMPLY A LACK OF PROFESSIONALISM ON YOUR PART?
WOW! MUST YOU ALWAYS THINK IN SUCH CAREERIST TERMS, ALEX?

IS THERE SOMETHING WRONG WITH WANTING TO TAKE A BIT OF TIME OFF TO SPEND WITH ONE'S FAMILY, TO READ, RELAX, TRAVEL... AND GET PAID FOR IT?
NO, NO, OF COURSE NOT...

IT'S WHAT GARDENING LEAVE IS FOR... BUT THIS WILL JUST REMIND PEOPLE THAT NO-ONE'S WANTED TO HEADHUNT YOU FOR A DECADE...
OH GOD...
RIP
RIP

Alex
PEATTIE+TAYLOR
DID YOU BOOK, ALEX?
NO NEED... THE MAITRE D', STEFANO WILL FIND US A TABLE.
alex@alexcartoon.com

AH YES: STEFANO. HE'S BEEN AT THIS PLACE FOR 25 YEARS AND HIS NAME IS SYNONYMOUS WITH ITS REPUTATION AS THE BEST RESTAURANT IN THE CITY...
AH, MR MASTERLEY. TABLE FOR TWO?

HOLD ON A MINUTE, STEFANO... PAUL, WOULD YOU LIKE TO BE OUTSIDE OR INSIDE?
INSIDE PLEASE

GOOD... SO HERE'S THE LOWDOWN: STEFANO'S DEFECTING NEXT WEEK SO IF YOU OWN ANY SHARES IN THIS PLACE SELL THEM QUICK...
SHH, MR MASTERLEY. I HAVE NOT TOLD MY BOSS I'M LEAVING YET...
THANKS FOR THE TIP, ALEX.
TAP
TAP

Alex
PEATTIE+TAYLOR
SO WHAT ARE THESE HEDGE FUNDS THAT YOU WANT TO WORK IN, CHRISTOPHER?
TRADED FUNDS THAT INVEST MONEY FOR RICH INDIVIDUALS, PENNY...
alex@alexcartoon.com

THEY USE HIGH-RISK STRATEGIES AND TYPICALLY CHARGE A 2% MANAGEMENT FEE AND TAKE 20% OF ANY PROFITS. THE SUCCESSFUL ONES ATTRACT A LOT OF MONEY...
THEY MUST BECOME VERY LARGE...

YES, BUT THERE'S A MAXIMUM SIZE AT WHICH THEY ARE PRACTICABLE...
YES, MUM, YOU SEE IF YOUR FUND IS TOO BIG YOU HAVE TO TRADE IN SUCH LARGE VOLUMES THAT YOU MOVE THE MARKET...
ER, ACTUALLY CHRISTOPHER...

I MEANT THAT IF ONE IS MAKING 2% OF, SAY, $1.5 BILLION FOR JUST DOING NOTHING HOW HARD WOULD ONE ACTUALLY BOTHER TO WORK?

Alex
PEATTIE+TAYLOR
CYRUS IS PROPOSING THAT WE SHOULD NO LONGER RECEIVE THE AIR MILES FROM OUR BUSINESS TRAVEL...
AH YES. MANAGEMENT TRIES THIS FROM TIME TO TIME...
alex@alexcartoon.com

IT WILL BE MET WITH STIFF RESISTANCE. AIR MILES ARE A TRADITIONAL PERK OF OUR JOBS...
HE'S GOT A POINT IN A SENSE, ALEX... AFTER ALL THE BANK DOES PAY FOR OUR FLIGHTS...

IF IT WERE TO GET THE AIR MILES THEY COULD BE CHANNELLED BACK INTO PAYING FOR OUR BUSINESS TRAVEL. SUCH A POLICY WOULD RESULT IN A CONSIDERABLE COST SAVING...
IT CERTAINLY WOULD.

AS SOON AS THEY REALISED 75% OF OUR BUSINESS TRIPS WERE COMPLETELY UNNECESSARY AND WE'D ONLY BEEN DOING THEM TO BUMP UP OUR AIR MILES FUND...
HEM HEM... YES THAT WOULD BE AWKWARD.

Alex
PEATTIE + TAYLOR
HELLO, MR MASTERLEY, THIS IS STEFANO – THE EX-MAITRE D' AT LE GOURMET...
alex@alexcartoon.com

HELLO, STEFANO... ARE YOU OFFICIALLY ALLOWED TO CONTACT ME? I THOUGHT YOU WERE ON GARDENING LEAVE...
YES, I START AT MY NEW RESTAURANT, JONES'S, NEXT WEEK...

BUT THE PROPRIETOR IS VERY WORRIED. HE WAS HOPING TO BE ABLE TO COUNT ON THE LOYALTY OF MY OLD CUSTOMERS... BUT HE HASN'T HAD A SINGLE RESERVATION FROM ANY OF YOU...
OF COURSE NOT...

...WHY WOULD WE BOOK IN ADVANCE? THE WHOLE POINT ABOUT KNOWING THE MAITRE D' IS TO IMPRESS ONE'S GUESTS BY GETTING A TABLE AT SHORT NOTICE...

Alex
PEATTIE + TAYLOR
SO YOU'VE DECIDED TO GIVE UP SMOKING, ALEX?
WELL, WITH THIS PUBLIC SMOKING BAN COMING INTO FORCE NEXT MONTH...
alex@alexcartoon.com

ARE YOU CONFIDENT OF BEING ABLE TO MANAGE IT THIS TIME?
LET'S HOPE SO... ON THE PREVIOUS OCCASION THAT I QUIT I LASTED 6 WEEKS...

IT'S ALL ABOUT WORKING TOWARDS OBJECTIVES, TARGETS, DEADLINES... IT'S BEST TO HAVE SOME KEY DATE IN MIND... LAST TIME IT WAS JANUARY 1ST...
THAT'S WHEN YOU GAVE UP?

NO THAT'S WHEN I STARTED AGAIN. I'D PUT ON A STONE, AND GOING BACK ON THE CIGS GAVE ME THE EDGE IN THE OFFICE NEW YEAR WEIGHT LOSS COMPETITION...

Alex
PEATTIE + TAYLOR
EBAY REALLY IS A MOST VALUABLE RESOURCE FOR GETTING RID OF UNWANTED ITEMS ONE WOULD PREVIOUSLY HAVE HAD TO GIVE AWAY...
alex@alexcartoon.com

BECAUSE IT'S AN ONLINE AUCTION THAT COULD POTENTIALLY BE SEEN BY MILLIONS OF BIDDERS WORLDWIDE, ONE CAN BE PRETTY SURE OF GETTING A FAIR PRICE...

LOOK, FOR EXAMPLE... THE AUCTION'S JUST FINISHED ON THE VARIOUS ITEMS THAT I'M SELLING... YOUR SIGNED PHOTO OF THE ENGLAND CRICKET TEAM WENT FOR £125....
OH YES...

NOWHERE NEAR THE £2,000 YOU DRUNKENLY PAID FOR IT AT THAT CHARITY AUCTION LAST WEEK... NEED ANY MORE PROOF, IDIOT?
ER, NO... YOU MADE YOUR VIEWS ON THE MATTER CLEAR AT THE TIME...

Alex
PEATTIE + TAYLOR
SEE THAT GUY? THAT IS SO TYPICAL OF THE BEHAVIOUR OF BUSINESS CLASS PASSENGERS.
ELBOW
alex@alexcartoon.com

DELIBERATELY BOARDING THE FLIGHT AT THE LAST POSSIBLE MOMENT AND THEN ON TOUCHDOWN FIGHTING TO GET OFF THE PLANE FIRST AND PRACTICALLY SPRINTING DOWN THE GANGWAY..

IT'S ALL PART OF THEIR COMPETITIVE NEED TO SHOW WHO'S THE MOST IMPORTANT... TO GET THE MAXIMUM WORK TIME IN BEFORE TAKE-OFF AND THEN BE FIRST IN THE TAXI QUEUE ON ARRIVAL...

SO YOU WERE IN BUSINESS CLASS AND YOUR CLIENT WAS IN ECONOMY ON THE SAME PLANE? HOW DID YOU AVOID HAVING TO OFFER HIM YOUR SEAT?
PRETENDED I WAS ON A DIFFERENT FLIGHT AND MADE DAMNED SURE HE DIDN'T SPOT ME.

Alex
PEATTIE + TAYLOR
WHAT? YOU'RE GOING ON A LADS' BOOZY NIGHT OUT ON FRIDAY? HOW PATHETIC. WHY DO YOU NEED TO DO THAT?

I DON'T KNOW, DARLING... IT'S A MALE THING... I SUPPOSE IT'S A THROWBACK TO TRIBAL BEHAVIOUR WITH MEN NEEDING TO REAFFIRM EACH OTHER'S STATUS WITHIN THE GROUP...
BUT YOU'RE A STOCKBROKER, NOT A CAVEMAN...
alex@alexcartoon.com

WHAT CAN I SAY...? SOMETIMES A BUNCH OF MATES JUST FEEL LIKE GOING OUT TOGETHER FOR A FEW BEERS ON A FRIDAY NIGHT...
OKAY...

BUT WHY DO THEY ALWAYS NEED YOU TO GO ALONG WITH THEM? YOU'RE NOT EVEN THEIR FRIEND.
ONE OF THEM'S A HEDGE FUND CLIENT OF MINE AND HE EXPECTS ME TO BE THERE TO PICK UP THE TAB...

Alex
PEATTIE + TAYLOR
THE MAITRE D' WAS VERY EFFUSIVE...
MENU
JONES'S
STEFANO? YES, HE'S JUST STARTED WORKING HERE AFTER A MONTH'S GARDENING LEAVE...

I'VE MISSED HIS EXPERTISE, PENNY. HE REALLY IS THE BEST...
WHAT? JUST BECAUSE HE MADE LOUD PROFESSIONS OF DELIGHT AT SEEING YOU AFTER ALL THIS TIME?
JONES'S
alex@alexcartoon.com

DOES YOUR EGO REALLY NEED THAT, ALEX? ALL THAT FALSENESS AND FAWNING AND FLATTERY? IS THAT WHAT MAKES HIM SO GOOD AT HIS JOB TO YOUR EYES?
JONES'S

STEFANO, THAT GENTLEMAN: HE WAS HERE YESTERDAY WITH A DIFFERENT LADY...
HIS MISTRESS... BUT WE DON'T SAY A WORD...

Alex
PEATTIE + TAYLOR
SO YOU'RE THINKING OF BECOMING CHAIRMAN OF A CHARITY, RUPERT?
IT'S AN AREA I HAVE A PERSONAL INTEREST IN, ALEX...

AND AFTER ALL I'VE SPENT 35 YEARS AS AN INVESTMENT BANKER, DRIVEN BY MATERIALISM, AMBITION AND COMPETITIVENESS IN PURSUIT OF PERSONAL AND PURELY COMMERCIAL GOALS...

alex@alexcartoon.com

AS ONE GETS OLDER ONE WONDERS WHAT SORT OF MESSAGE ONE IS SENDING OUT AND STARTS TO FEEL THAT THE CHARITABLE SECTOR MIGHT BE A MORE WORTHWHILE PLACE TO WORK...

BECAUSE IT SHOWS EVERYONE THAT YOU REALLY DON'T NEED THE MONEY ANY MORE?
QUITE... THAT'S THE IMPORTANT THING...

Alex
PEATTIE + TAYLOR
IF YOU'RE HAVING DIFFICULTY GIVING UP CIGARETTES ON YOUR OWN, ALEX, PERHAPS YOU SHOULD GO TO ONE OF THOSE STOP SMOKING CLINICS.
alex@alexcartoon.com

YOU'D BE WITH PEOPLE FROM ALL DIFFERENT WALKS OF LIFE WITH WHOM YOU'LL BE ABLE TO COMPARE EXPERIENCES OF HOW SMOKING HAS IMPACTED ON YOU...

PLUS THE CLINICS ARE RUN BY THERAPISTS WHO ARE TRAINED IN HOW TO GET ACROSS THE DETRIMENTAL EFFECTS OF NICOTINE ADDICTION IN REALISTIC, PRACTICAL TERMS.

OVER YOUR LIFETIME SMOKING COULD COST YOU ¥ 250,000
THAT'S LESS THAN A HALF OF WHAT MY LAST YEAR'S BONUS WAS...

Alex
PEATTIE + TAYLOR
YOU ARE A GROUP OF PEOPLE FROM DIFFERENT WALKS OF LIFE, BROUGHT TOGETHER BY YOUR COMMON DESIRE TO QUIT SMOKING.

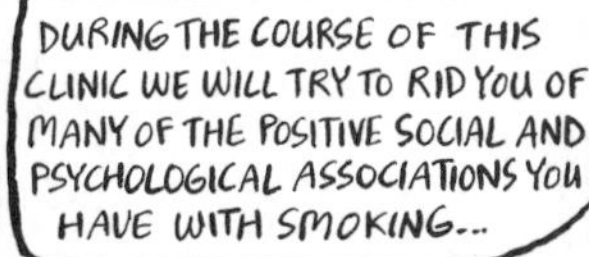
DURING THE COURSE OF THIS CLINIC WE WILL TRY TO RID YOU OF MANY OF THE POSITIVE SOCIAL AND PSYCHOLOGICAL ASSOCIATIONS YOU HAVE WITH SMOKING...

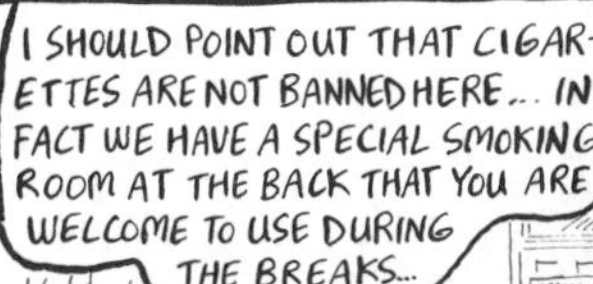
I SHOULD POINT OUT THAT CIGARETTES ARE NOT BANNED HERE... IN FACT WE HAVE A SPECIAL SMOKING ROOM AT THE BACK THAT YOU ARE WELCOME TO USE DURING THE BREAKS...
SMOKING ROOM

THIS IS NO FUN... IT'S NOT LIKE HANGING AROUND OUTSIDE ONE'S OWN OFFICE BLOCK...
WE DON'T KNOW ANYONE IN COMMON TO GOSSIP ABOUT...
OR HAVE ANY INTERNAL RUMOURS TO SPREAD...
SMOKING ROOM
I THINK THE THERAPY'S WORKING.

Alex
PEATTIE + TAYLOR
IT'S CONSIDERATE OF THE ORGANISERS OF THIS STOP SMOKING CLINIC TO PROVIDE US WITH A SMOKING ROOM.
YES...

FUNNY TO THINK THAT THESE COULD BE OUR VERY FINAL CIGARETTES...
WELL, WITH THIS BAN ON SMOKING IN ALL PUBLIC BUILDINGS COMING IN NEXT MONTH IT SEEMS SENSIBLE.

AND THANKS TO THE CLINIC WE'VE NOW DEFINITELY DECIDED TO KICK THE HABIT.
ALL THE SAME IT'S STRANGE TO REALISE THAT WE'RE AT THE END OF AN ERA...

I MEAN WE MAY JUST HAVE MADE ONE OF THE LAST EVER DECISIONS TO BE TAKEN IN A "SMOKE-FILLED ROOM"..
SIGH YES... CLICHÉS WILL NEVER BE THE SAME AGAIN...

Alex
PEATTIE + TAYLOR
WELL, EVERYONE, WE'VE NOW REACHED THE END OF OUR STOP SMOKING CLINIC.

THIS IS THE TIME FOR YOU TO GO THROUGH WITH YOUR RESOLUTION. SO, AS YOU LEAVE THE ROOM, I INVITE YOU TO THROW YOUR CIGARETTES INTO THE BINLINERS PROVIDED.

REMEMBER: AS YOU LITERALLY AND SYMBOLICALLY RID YOURSELF OF SMOKING, YOU SHOULD FEEL A GREAT SENSE OF PRIDE AND PERSONAL SATISFACTION...

WOW! MONTECRISTO A'S! THEY COST £40 EACH...
WAIT TILL YOU SEE THE SOLID GOLD TIFFANY'S CIGAR CUTTER THAT'S GOING IN NEXT...

Alex
PEATTIE + TAYLOR
SO, WERE YOU ENTERTAINING CLIENTS AT ASCOT LAST WEEK, GRANT?
NO, I TOOK MINE TO GLASTONBURY..

THAT'S WHAT HIP CUSTOMERS WANT TO DO THESE DAYS: GO TO A ROCK FESTIVAL, CHILL OUT, LISTEN TO MUSIC AND PARTY ALL NIGHT.
ALL NIGHT? YOU MEAN YOU WERE ON DRUGS?

WELL OF COURSE... YOU KNOW THE BROKERS' MOTTO, CLIVE: GIVE THE CLIENT WHATEVER HE WANTS... YOU WOULD NOT BELIEVE WHAT SOME PEOPLE ARE CLAIMING TO HAVE TAKEN OVER THE LAST 48 HOURS...
TELL ME.

ER... WELL IN MY CASE: 27 TAXIS. I COULDN'T PERSUADE ANY OF THE DRUG DEALERS TO GIVE ME RECEIPTS SO I'M PUTTING IN LOTS OF FAKE CAB BILLS ON MY EXPENSES CLAIM...
SADLY I DON'T THINK MY BOSS WILL BELIEVE IT EITHER...

alex@alexcartoon.com

alex@alexcartoon.com

alex@alexcartoon.com

alex@alexcartoon.com

Alex
PEATTIE + TAYLOR
SADDLE UP, GUYS! I'VE BOOKED ALL OF US ON A TEAM BONDING EXERCISE IN THE U.S.
WHAT?

LIKE THE MOVIE "CITY SLICKERS"... WE'RE GONNA GO ON A CATTLE DRIVE! HORSES, WAGONS, TEN-GALLON HATS, CAMP FIRES, SLEEPING UNDER THE STARS...
BUT... BUT...
alex@alexcartoon.com

BUT CYRUS, WE'RE SOFT, INEXPERIENCED CITY FOLK... WE DON'T KNOW THE FIRST THING ABOUT THE ROUGH, TOUGH LIFE OUTSIDE THE PAMPERED SECURITY OF OUR OFFICE LIVES..
DON'T WORRY, GUYS... I ASKED AROUND ABOUT WHO TO BOOK WITH...

I'VE BEEN TOLD THE NAME OF THE BIGGEST COWBOY TOUR OPERATOR IN THE BUSINESS. WE'RE IN SAFE HANDS...
I HAVE A BAD FEELING ABOUT THIS...

Alex
PEATTIE + TAYLOR
WHOAH! LOOK AT THOSE GUYS IN THE CORRAL! THAT LOOKS LIKE TOUGH WORK.
YEE HA!
IT'S WHAT I PAID THEM FOR...
KICK
PRANCE
YOU PAID THEM? WHY?

TRUST ME: I COULD LOOK REAL FOOLISH IF I TRIED TO RIDE OUT OF HERE WITHOUT THOSE GUYS DOING THEIR JOBS FIRST...
WHOAH!
BOOF
alex@alexcartoon.com

THERE YOU ARE, DUDE. I RECKON WE GOT THEM BROKEN IN FOR YOU REAL GOOD..
YOU CERTAINLY DID. THANK YOU.
SWEAT
PUFF
PANT
THEY HAVE TO BREAK IN THE HORSES?

NO, NO... MY NEW DENIM TROUSERS. I DON'T WANT TO LOOK LIKE A TOWNIE, DO I?
THANKS CHAPS.
YOU'RE WELCOME.
HERE Y'AR.

Alex
PEATTIE + TAYLOR
NOW LISTEN UP, FOLKS. WE'RE HEADING OUT ON THE TRAIL... IT'S GRITTY AND TOUGH AND NOT FOR THE SOFT...

BUT IT'S THE AUTHENTIC COWBOY EXPERIENCE AND THAT'S HOW WE LIKE IT... THE GREAT OUTDOORS, SLEEPING IN THE OPEN, EATING ROUND A FIRE... ARE YOU READY FOR IT?
YES, SIREE!
alex@alexcartoon.com

YOU GOTTA UNDERSTAND HOW SERIOUSLY WE TAKE CAMPING AROUND HERE... THERE'S NO FRILLS ON THIS TOUR...
OKAY.

AND NO FANCY EMBROIDERY NEITHER.. NO ONE'S GONNA GO CAMPING AROUND IN A SHIRT LIKE THIS ONE...
BUT IT'S FROM A GENUINE COWBOY OUTFITTER... IT COST OVER $300...
FLUTTER
THIS AIN'T BROKEBACK MOUNTAIN, MISTER. GET RID OF IT...

Alex
PEATTIE + TAYLOR
I WISH YOU WOULDN'T BY SO PATRONISING... I'M NOT A TOTAL IGNORAMUS.
JUST TRYING TO BE FRIENDLY, PODNER...

LOOK, I KNOW WE'RE GOING OUT ON A CATTLE DRIVE, I REALISE WE'LL BE LASSOOING CATTLE AND I DO HAVE THE CORRECT KIT FOR IT..
alex@alexcartoon.com

BUT EVERYONE KEEPS ASKING "WHERE'S YOUR ROPE?"... "WHERE'S YOUR ROPE?"...
PAT PAT
WELL, FOR YOUR INFORMATION IT'S RIGHT HERE, SECURELY FASTENED TO MY SADDLE...

NO, I MEAN: WHERE'S "YEUR-OPE"? THE COUNTRY...?
OH... ER, IT'S LIKE, A BIG BIT OF LAND EAST OF NEW YORK...
WHOAH!

Alex
PEATTIE+TAYLOR
HEY, WHAT'S THAT?
OH JUST A BIG TUBE OF OINTMENT I'M CARRYING FOR OUR TENDERFOOT FRIENDS...

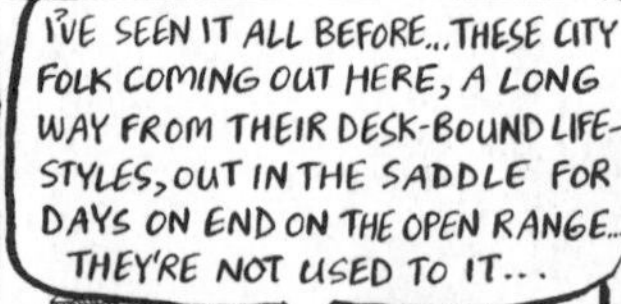
I'VE SEEN IT ALL BEFORE... THESE CITY FOLK COMING OUT HERE, A LONG WAY FROM THEIR DESK-BOUND LIFE-STYLES, OUT IN THE SADDLE FOR DAYS ON END ON THE OPEN RANGE... THEY'RE NOT USED TO IT...

alex@alexcartoon.com

AND WHAT WITH THE MOTION OF THE HORSE AND THE PREDICTABLE CONSTANT RUBBING PRESSURE AS THEY RIDE ALONG... I'M AFRAID THEY GET SORES IN THE OBVIOUS PLACE...

THEIR EARS?
YUP. 'COS THEY'RE ON THEIR PHONES ALL DAY...
HELLO? I'M ON THE HORSE... OUCH!
EXCUSE ME? HAS ANY-BODY GOT ANYTHING FOR A SORE EAR...?

Alex
PEATTIE+TAYLOR
SSSSS... RATTLE RATTLE -RATTLE...
HEY, SHH!...
YOU HEAR THAT NOISE? IT'S COMING FROM BEHIND THAT ROCK...
WHAT IS IT, CYRUS?

alex@alexcartoon.com
SSSSSS... RATTLE RATTLE... SSSS... RATTLE...
THE HISSING AND THE TELL-TALE RATTLE...? YOU GUYS REALLY ARE A BUNCH OF GREEN HORNS AREN'T YOU? YOU'RE NOT FIT FOR THE OPEN RANGE AT ALL...
SSSSS...

I'M GONNA CREEP UP ON THAT VARMIT AND CATCH HIM BY SURPRISE...
SSSS... RATTLE RATTLE... SSSSS...

HEY! I TOLD YOU TO BRAND THOSE CATTLE, YOU WIMPS! NOT SPRAY STENCIL THEM...
BUT IT'S SO BARBARIC...
RATTLE RATTLE
SHAKE
SPRAY PAINT
PAINT MAGIC
PAINT
SSSS...

Alex
PEATTIE+TAYLOR
OKAY, WE'RE GONNA START AGAIN... YOU KNOW WHAT A BRAND IS?
SEE THIS FAINT "X" SHAPE? THAT'S WHERE IT WAS BRANDED BEFORE...

alex@alexcartoon.com
BUT YOU HAVE TO KEEP DOING IT OVER AND OVER AGAIN... IT'S A TOUGH, SKILLED JOB AND IT NEEDS TO BE DONE RIGHT...

I NEED PEOPLE WHO ARE GOING TO BRAND THIS HERD PROPERLY...
HEY, LEAVE IT TO US, CYRUS WE'LL SORT IT OUT FOR YOU...

WHAT THE HELL'S THIS?!
WE GOT A CREATIVE TEAM IN AND THEY SUGGESTED A WAVY BLUE LINE UNDERNEATH THE 'X' AND CHARGED US $1 MILLION DESIGN FEE FOR A NEW LOGO.
MAYBE TASKING IT TO CORPORATE COMMS WAS A BAD IDEA...
INVOICE

Alex
PEATTIE+TAYLOR
HOW GOES IT, CYRUS?
WELL WATCHING OVER THE STOCK IS QUITE A CHALLENGE. YOU CAN'T AFFORD TO TAKE YOUR EYES OFF THEM FOR A MOMENT...
MOO
MOO
MOO

YOU NEVER KNOW WHEN SOME-THING MIGHT SUDDENLY SPOOK THEM AND MAKE THEM MOVE OFF WITHOUT WARNING... AND THERE'S NOTHING YOU CAN DO ABOUT IT...

MOO
alex@alexcartoon.com

EXCEPT JUST RIDE ALONG WITH THEM AND TRY TO STAY AHEAD OF THEM, WHEREVER THEY'RE GOING... THEY ALL JUST FOLLOW EACH OTHER AS THE HERD INSTINCT TAKES OVER.
MOO
MOO
I GUESS SO...

YUP... THE MARKET'S A STRANGE THING TO KEEP TRACK OF...
ER... CYRUS? WHAT ABOUT ALL THE STEERS?
GLOW
NO... YOU CAN'T TRUST WHAT THE ANALYSTS GIVE YOU, EITHER...

GLOW
GLOW
GLOW
GLOW
GLOW
DEAD

GENUINE
COWBOY OUTFITTERS
LET'S DO LYNCH.
YUP

Alex
PEATTIE+TAYLOR
HERE WE ARE... SLEEPING UNDER THE OPEN SKY, EATING HOME COOKING OFF A CAMP FIRE... TRAVELLING EVERYWHERE ON HORSEBACK OR JUST ROAMING AROUND ON FOOT...THE SIMPLE LIFE IN THE GREAT OUTDOORS...

WHEN YOU'RE LIVING LIKE THIS YOU CAN EASILY FORGET THE OTHER SIDE OF HUMAN NATURE... THE GREED, OPPORTUNISM, CUNNING AND DISHONESTY...BUT I GUESS IT'S ALWAYS WITH US...
WHAT DO YOU MEAN..?

WELL, I'VE HEARD SOME RUSTLING'S GOING ON IN THESE PARTS...
REALLY?
YUP...
alex@alexcartoon.com

OVER THERE. IT'S ALEX... TYPICAL.
HOW THE HECK HE ACQUIRED ANY RECEIPTS OUT HERE TO CHARGE ON HIS EXPENSES IS A TOTAL MYSTERY....
ZZZ...
ZZ
RUSTLE RUSTLE
RECEIPT

Alex
PEATTIE+TAYLOR
I'M SURPRISED, CLIVE... YOU DID PRETTY GOOD IN THAT GUN FIGHT.
GUN FIGHT TEST YOUR REFLEXES
SALOON
SHERIFF
OH I'VE PRACTISED THE REQUISITE SKILLS...
alex@alexcartoon.com

YOU SEE, THE PISTOL GRIP IS SECOND NATURE TO ME...AND HAVING A STEADY FINGER ON THE TRIGGER... KEEPING MY EYE ON THE TARGET...

AND THEN TIMING: WAITING UNTIL THE VERY LAST MOMENT WHEN I MAKE MY MOVE...
AND PUMP THE SUCKER FULL OF LEAD, RIGHT?

WELL, LEAD-FREE THESE DAYS OF COURSE...
IT'S A MATTER OF PERSONAL PRIDE TO GET AN EXACTLY ROUND FIGURE'S WORTH OF PETROL, BRIDGET...
YOU'RE SUCH A WIMP, CLIVE.
WHIRR WHIRR
PRICE 14·93
PETROL
CONCENTRATION

Alex
PEATTIE+TAYLOR
BEING UMPIRE IS A VERY DEMANDING AND RESPONSIBLE ROLE, ALEX, EVEN IN A CHARITY CRICKET MATCH
CHARITY CRICKET IN AID OF Wellbeing for Women
alex@alexcartoon.com

SUNIL GAVASKAR MAY BE ONE OF THE GREATEST BATSMEN IN THE HISTORY OF THE GAME, BUT WHEN HE WAS HIT ON THE PADS BY A STRAIGHT BALL I HAD NO HESITATION IN GIVING HIM OUT L.B.W...

I SHALL ALWAYS REMEMBER THE AUTHORITATIVE, ASSURED AND DECISIVE WAY I RAISED MY INDEX FINGER...
YOU CERTAINLY WILL

YOU'VE JUST PAID ¥8,000 FOR A HARRODS PICNIC HAMPER...
SOLD! TO THE GENTLEMAN IN THE GLASSES...
WHAT..? OH NO...
BANG
AUCTION

Alex
PEATTIE+TAYLOR
ONCE UPON A TIME ONE COULD DO PRETTY MUCH ANYTHING TO WIN A CLIENT'S BUSINESS...

BUT THESE DAYS IT'S ALL BEEN OUTLAWED BY THE STRINGENT NEW RULES PERTAINING TO ENTERTAINMENT, THE GIVING OF GIFTS ETC...
THAT'S ALL PART OF THE MODERN COMPLIANCE REGIME, ALEX...
alex@alexcartoon.com

EXACTLY. IT'S LED TO AN ETHOS WHERE WE'RE ALL SCARED OF STEPPING OUT OF LINE AND FEEL THAT OUR EVERY WORD AND ACTION IS BEING CLOSELY MONITORED AND SCRUTINISED...

BY OUR CLIENTS' CHILDREN?
QUITE... GIVING INTERNSHIPS TO THEIR USELESS OFFSPRING IS NOW THE ONLY WAY WE CAN BRIBE CLIENTS TO DO BUSINESS WITH US...

Alex
PEATTIE + TAYLOR
PENNY, THAT QUIT SMOKING CLINIC I WENT TO LAST MONTH... HAVE YOU BEEN IN CONTACT WITH THEM?
ACTUALLY, YES...
GOSSIP
alex@alexcartoon.com

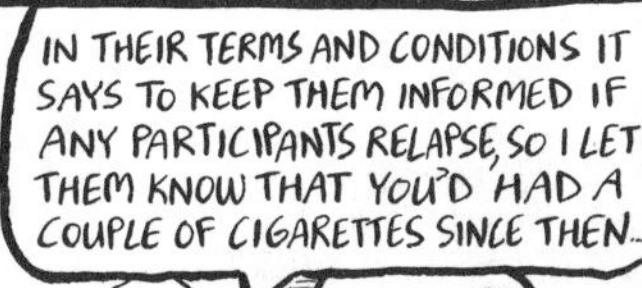
IN THEIR TERMS AND CONDITIONS IT SAYS TO KEEP THEM INFORMED IF ANY PARTICIPANTS RELAPSE, SO I LET THEM KNOW THAT YOU'D HAD A COUPLE OF CIGARETTES SINCE THEN...

WHAT...?!

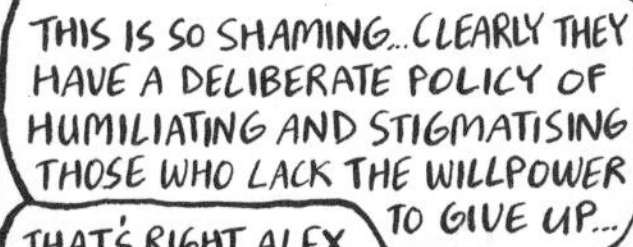
THIS IS SO SHAMING... CLEARLY THEY HAVE A DELIBERATE POLICY OF HUMILIATING AND STIGMATISING THOSE WHO LACK THE WILLPOWER TO GIVE UP...

THAT'S RIGHT, ALEX...
GOSSIP

IT'S CALLED THEIR "MONEY BACK GUARANTEE"...
THEY'VE SENT ME A CHEQUE... DO I LOOK LIKE SOMEONE WHO'S SHORT OF £230?

Alex
PEATTIE + TAYLOR
SO WHAT'S THIS RIDICULOUS NEW EXERCISE THE BANK HAS JUST ANNOUNCED?
"UPGRADING THE WORKFORCE"...
alex@alexcartoon.com

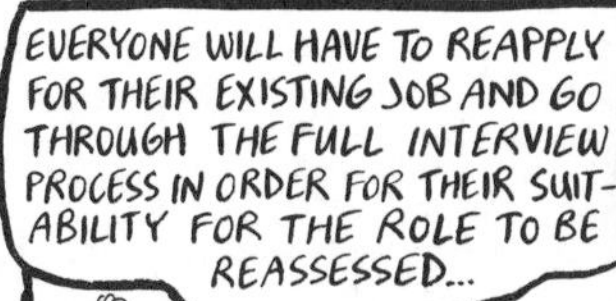
EVERYONE WILL HAVE TO REAPPLY FOR THEIR EXISTING JOB AND GO THROUGH THE FULL INTERVIEW PROCESS IN ORDER FOR THEIR SUITABILITY FOR THE ROLE TO BE REASSESSED...

WELL, WITH THE BANK IN TAKEOVER TALKS, THERE WILL BE A NEED FOR REDUNDANCIES AND AN EXERCISE LIKE THIS WILL GIVE US A CLEAR IDEA OF WHO IS SURPLUS TO REQUIREMENTS...
YES...

THE WHOLE HUMAN RESOURCES DEPARTMENT FOR CREATING ALL THIS GRATUITOUS ACTIVITY JUST TO APPEAR BUSY AND USEFUL...
THAT WOULD MAKE SENSE. SADLY IT DOESN'T WORK LIKE THAT...

Alex
PEATTIE + TAYLOR
I DON'T BELIEVE IT... MY ENTIRE DEPARTMENT HAS TO REINTERVIEW FOR THEIR JOBS?
IT'S A NONSENSE I AGREE, ALEX...
alex@alexcartoon.com

THINGS HAVE CERTAINLY CHANGED IN THE CITY SINCE I DID MY FIRST INTERVIEW, CONDUCTED BY YOURSELF, RUPERT, 20 YEARS AGO...
WELL, THE BASICS HAVE REMAINED PRETTY MUCH THE SAME, ALEX...

THE FUNCTION OF THE INTERVIEW HAS ALWAYS BEEN TO PROVIDE A CHALLENGING ENVIRONMENT IN WHICH TO TEST A CANDIDATE'S ABILITY TO DEMONSTRATE CLEAR LEVEL-HEADED THINKING...
YES...

I REMEMBER: MINE WAS HELD OVER A SIX-HOUR LUNCH AND I GOT THE JOB BECAUSE I WAS THE ONLY PERSON SOBER ENOUGH TO SETTLE THE BILL AFTERWARDS.
AH YES... THOSE WERE THE DAYS...

Alex
PEATTIE + TAYLOR
THE BANK IS "UPGRADING ITS WORKFORCE" WHICH MEANS WE ALL HAVE TO REAPPLY FOR OUR JOBS HERE.
alex@alexcartoon.com

SENIOR BANKERS SUCH AS MYSELF WILL HAVE TO SUFFER THE INDIGNITY OF DOING A FORMAL JOB INTERVIEW, WHEN I BELIEVE MY TALENTS GO WITHOUT SAYING...
I AGREE...

THIS WHOLE EXERCISE IS UTTERLY INSENSITIVE, WHEN ONE CONSIDERS ALL THE YEARS I'VE WORKED AT MEGABANK AND WHAT I'VE ACHIEVED HERE...

I'VE GOT IT TO A STAGE WHERE NO ONE REMEMBERS WHAT MY JOB IS... DO I REALLY WANT THEM TO REALISE THAT NOW...?
IT'S A SCARY THOUGHT...

Alex
PEATTIE + TAYLOR
SO, CYRUS, YOU'RE MAKING THE WHOLE DEPARTMENT REAPPLY FOR THEIR JOBS?
YEAH. IT'S CALLED "UPGRADING THE WORKFORCE"...

BUT SURELY YOU WORK THOSE GUYS HARD ENOUGH AS IT IS... DO YOU REALLY NEED TO PUT MORE STRESS ON THEM?
IT'LL BE A USEFUL EXPERIENCE FOR THEM...
alex@alexcartoon.com

HAVING TO GO THROUGH A FORMAL INTERVIEW PROCESS AND ANSWER STANDARD QUESTIONS WILL HELP REMIND THEM OF THE FUNDA-MENTALS OF THEIR JOBS...

SO, WHAT DO YOU LIKE TO DO IN YOUR SPARE TIME?
ER... I REALLY CAN'T REMEMBER... IT'S BEEN SUCH A LONG TIME SINCE I HAD ANY...
RIGHT AND THAT'S THE WAY IT'S GONNA STAY...

Alex
PEATTIE + TAYLOR
SO THE BANK IS "UPGRADING ITS WORKFORCE" AND MAKING US ALL INTERVIEW FOR OUR POSITIONS HERE?
YES.

PEOPLE AREN'T TAKING THE THREAT TO THEIR JOBS LIGHTLY. SOME, LIKE CHRISTIAN, ARE DOING SERIOUS PREPARATION, PRINTING OUT DETAILS OF THE BANK AND ITS BUSINESS...
PRINT PRINT
alex@alexcartoon.com

IT'S REMARKABLE THAT CERTAIN INDIVIDUALS SHOULD STILL NEED TO BE FAMILIARISED WITH SUCH BASIC INFORMATION AS THE BANK'S CLIENT LIST...
CLIENT LIST

SEE THIS COMPANY? MY DAD IS C.E.O. AND THEY PAID US £35M IN FEES LAST YEAR... NOW, DO WE NEED TO GO ON WITH THIS?
AH... ER....
CLIENT LIST

Alex
PEATTIE + TAYLOR
THIS EXTREME WEATHER IS JUST FURTHER EVIDENCE THAT CLIMATE CHANGE IS NOW A REALITY...
FLOODS

THERE CAN BE NO DOUBT NOW THAT HUMANITY NEEDS TO TAKE RADICAL ACTION IF CATASTROPHE ON A GLOBAL SCALE IS TO BE AVERTED...
alex@alexcartoon.com

SO HOW DO THOSE PEOPLE WHO SELFISHLY REFUSED TO MAKE THE LIFESTYLE CHANGES TO CUT THEIR CARBON EMISSIONS FEEL NOW..?

RATHER SMUG ACTUALLY... MY 4×4 WAS JUST ABOUT THE ONLY WAY TO GET THROUGH THOSE FLOODS THIS WEEK...

Alex
PEATTIE + TAYLOR
SO THIS AFTERNOON YOUR WHOLE TEAM HAVE TO REINTERVIEW FOR THEIR JOBS, CYRUS?
THAT'S RIGHT.

IT'S PROVING TO BE A VERY INFORMATIVE EXERCISE...
BUT IT MUST BE CONFUSING FOR THEM HAVING TO DO AN INTERVIEW WITH SOMEONE WHO'S ALREADY THEIR BOSS...
alex@alexcartoon.com

I'VE TOLD THEM THEY HAVE TO DIFFER-ENTIATE MY TWO ROLES IN THEIR MINDS: ON THE ONE HAND I'M THEIR DEPARTMENT HEAD, BUT I'M ALSO A GUY WHO'S CONSIDERING THEM FOR A JOB.
AND HAVE THEY MANAGED TO DO IT?
SOME OF THEM YEAH...

CLIVE CAME IN AND TOLD ME HE HAS A DENTAL APPOINTMENT THIS AFTERNOON....
YOU IDIOT, CLIVE...
WELL THAT'S MY STANDARD COVER STORY TO MY BOSS WHEN I HAVE TO GO TO AN INTERVIEW...

Alex
PEATTIE + TAYLOR
BEFORE I REINTERVIEW YOU FOR YOUR JOB, BRIAN, I'D LIKE YOU TO SUMMARISE YOUR ROLE HERE
OKAY.

FRANKLY I DO NOTHING USEFUL FOR THE BANK. I SIT IN AN OFFICE, I TAKE LONG LUNCHES, I SURF THE INTERNET AND PHONE MY FRIENDS...
I SEE...
alex@alexcartoon.com

WELL, THANK YOU FOR YOUR CANDOUR. IN VIEW OF WHAT YOU'VE JUST SAID I'VE GOT TO INFORM YOU ABOUT THE CHANCES OF YOUR NAME BEING PLACED ON THE REDUNDANCY LIST...

NONE AT ALL... YOU'RE CLEARLY AWARE THAT WE'VE MOVED YOU INTO A NON-JOB AS IT'S TOO EXPENSIVE TO PAY YOU OFF... NOW CAN'T YOU TAKE THE HINT AND RESIGN...

Alex
PEATTIE + TAYLOR
GETTING OUR STAFF TO REAPPLY FOR THEIR JOBS IS A WAY TO WEED OUT THE WEAKER CANDIDATES...

THE RESULTS HAVE BEEN MOST ENLIGHTENING...TAKE ALEX FOR EXAMPLE: HE'S ONE OF OUR MOST EXPERIENCED AND LONG-SERVING BANKERS, YET HE PERFORMED BADLY AT INTERVIEW...
alex@alexcartoon.com

HE WAS ILL-PREPARED, UNRESPONSIVE, LACKED TECHNICAL AND BUSINESS SKILLS AND GENERALLY SCORED BADLY IN ALL DEPARTMENTS...
YES WELL THAT'S CLEAR THEN...

OBVIOUSLY HE WANTS US TO MAKE HIM REDUNDANT...
PRESUMABLY ANOTHER BANK HAS MADE HIM AN OFFER, SO THEY MUST THINK HE'S GOOD.
RIGHT. WE'D BETTER KEEP HIM THEN...

Alex
PEATTIE + TAYLOR
WITH THE INCREASINGLY COMPETITIVE JOB MARKET WE GET MORE SUMMER INTERNS THAN EVER THESE DAYS...

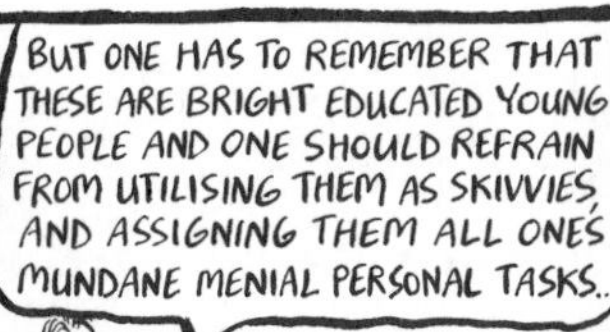
BUT ONE HAS TO REMEMBER THAT THESE ARE BRIGHT EDUCATED YOUNG PEOPLE AND ONE SHOULD REFRAIN FROM UTILISING THEM AS SKIVVIES, AND ASSIGNING THEM ALL ONE'S MUNDANE MENIAL PERSONAL TASKS...

alex@alexcartoon.com

THINGS HAVE CHANGED SINCE OUR DAY AND IT IS HARDLY CONDUCIVE TO HARMONIOUS OFFICE RELATIONS IF ONE GENERATION IS PERMITTED TO FLAUNT ITS SUPERIORITY OVER ANOTHER...

SO NEXT TIME YOU HAVE TO PRINT OUT YOUR C.V. DO IT YOURSELF
CLIVE'S ONLY GOT 3 A LEVELS AND 2 ARE GRADE B...
I'VE GOT 5... ALL "A PLUS." HOW DID HE GET A JOB?

Alex
PEATTIE + TAYLOR
SO YOU GOT A BOTTLE OF CHAMPAGNE TOO, ALEX?
YES, IT'S A PRESENT FROM A CLIENT...

I PRESUMED SO...ONE GETS THEM ALL THE TIME AS A TOKEN OF GRATITUDE FOR HAVING ORGANISED SOME DEAL... FRANKLY IT'S RATHER A DOWNMARKET BRAND... NOT EVEN VINTAGE...
THAT'S TRUE...
alex@alexcartoon.com

I MUST ADMIT I FOBBED MY BOTTLE OFF ON OUR SUMMER INTERN. HE'S TAKEN IT HOME. I TOLD HIM IT WAS PRETTY MUCH UNDRINKABLE AS FAR AS I WAS CONCERNED...
HMM... I'M NOT SURE I'D FEEL COMFORTABLE BEING THAT PATRONISING AND HIGH-HANDED...
TO AN INTERN...?

NO, TO HIS DAD: THE MAJOR CLIENT WHO SENT IT TO US AS A THANK YOU FOR GIVING HIS SON A JOB...
ER... OH GOD...

Alex
PEATTIE + TAYLOR
I MEANT TO ASK, DARLING... DO YOU LIKE MY NEW HANDBAG?
YES IT'S VERY NICE BUT YOU ALREADY SHOWED IT TO ME YESTERDAY...

DON'T BE SILLY, DARLING. THAT WAS THE OTHER BAG I BOUGHT AT THE SAME TIME... IT'S REALLY QUITE DIFFERENT...
IS IT?... ER, WELL THEY'RE BOTH NICE IN THAT CASE...
alex@alexcartoon.com

MEN! ALL THEY THINK ABOUT IS MONEY AND JOBS... WHEN IT COMES TO THE AESTHETIC THINGS IN LIFE THEY HAVE ABSOLUTELY NO JUDGEMENT OR APPRECIATION...
NO...

THANK GOODNESS... SO, YOU GOT THE £1500 Y.S.L. BAG... LOVELY.
I HAD THE SHOP PUT IT THROUGH ON TWO SEPARATE RECEIPTS SO HE WOULDN'T REALISE HOW MUCH IT COST...

Alex
PEATTIE + TAYLOR
WHAT DO YOU MEAN YOU HAVE TO GO, ALEX? YOU ONLY JUST ARRIVED....
SORRY, CAROLYN, BUT I PROMISED TO TAKE PENNY OUT TO DINNER...

alex@alexcartoon.com
LOOK, ALEX, I'VE BEEN YOUR MISTRESS FOR OVER A YEAR NOW... IS THIS THE WAY I'M ALWAYS GOING TO GET TREATED?
BUT WE'VE HAD A PLEASANT AFTER-WORK DRINK... A NICE CHAT...

AND NOW YOU'RE PROPOSING TO GO OFF AND BUY YOUR WIFE DINNER? IS THAT RIGHT? DONT I MEAN MORE THAN THAT TO YOU, ALEX?
PAT PAT
OF COURSE YOU DO, CAROLYN...

YOU'RE ALSO A CLIENT... WHICH MEANS I CAN EXPENSE THE DINNER... I'VE BEEN WITH YOU TONIGHT SO I CAN PUT THE REST OF MY EVENING ON MY ENTERTAINMENT BUDGET...

Alex
PEATTIE + TAYLOR
WITH THE BANK IN TAKEOVER TALKS OUR PRIORITY IS TO RETAIN STAFF, SO WE'VE GUARANTEED PEOPLE'S BONUSES THIS YEAR...

alex@alexcartoon.com
EVERYONE WILL BE PAID THE SAME AMOUNT AS THEY WERE LAST YEAR...
BUT WON'T THAT AFFECT OUR PROFITABILITY? AFTER ALL THE BONUS IS SUPPOSED TO INCENTIVISE PEOPLE TO WORK HARD...

WELL, NOT MUCH WORK GETS DONE AT THIS TIME OF YEAR ANYWAY...
BUT WHAT ABOUT AFTER THE SUMMER WHEN PEOPLE HABITUALLY COME BACK FROM THEIR HOLIDAY RESTED, REINVIGORATED AND FOCUSED?
YES...

AND THEN DEVOTE THE WHOLE OF THE LAST QUARTER TO LOBBYING FOR THEIR BONUSES...
TRUE... WE MAKE ALL OUR MONEY IN THE FIRST SIX MONTHS OF THE YEAR...

Alex
PEATTIE + TAYLOR
YOUR DEPARTMENT MUST HAVE BEEN PLEASED WHEN YOU TOLD THEM THAT AS A STAFF RETENTION MEASURE THEIR BONUSES ARE BEING GUARANTEED THIS YEAR...

alex@alexcartoon.com
YES... WELL, WITH MARKETS LOOKING A BIT ROCKY AT THE MOMENT I THINK THEY'RE ALL HAPPY TO SETTLE FOR BEING PAID THE SAME AMOUNT AS THEY GOT LAST YEAR...

AND AS HEAD OF DEPARTMENT I MUST SAY IT'S NICE TO HAVE AN OPPORTUNITY TO DELIVER SOME POSITIVE NEWS...

SO I'M LETTING EVERYONE KNOW THAT I'M BUYING A HELICOPTER...
WELL, FOR ONCE YOU DON'T HAVE TO MANAGE THEIR EXPECTATIONS...
SO THERE'S NO NEED TO BE COY ABOUT HOW MUCH MY BONUS WILL BE WORTH...

Alex
PEATTIE + TAYLOR
THE BANK HAS GUARANTEED THAT ALL STAFF WILL BE PAID THE SAME BONUSES AS LAST YEAR...
alex@alexcartoon.com

WE'RE THE TARGET OF A TAKEOVER BID AND THIS PLOY WILL HELP US TO HANG ON TO KEY PERSONNEL WHILE WE WORK OUT THE INEVITABLE REDUNDANCIES...
YES, OBVIOUSLY THERE ARE CERTAIN PEOPLE WE WOULDN'T WANT TO LOSE...

JAMES DANIELS IN MY DEPARTMENT FOR EXAMPLE...
ER, BUT CYRUS... DIDN'T YOU SAY THAT HE WAS SO USELESS THAT YOU PAID HIM A ZERO BONUS THIS YEAR?
YES...

BUT INSTEAD OF TAKING THE HINT AND RESIGNING HE'S BEEN HANGING ON FOR A REDUNDANCY CHEQUE...
SO WHEN HE DOESN'T GET ONE HE'LL BE REALLY HACKED OFF, ESPECIALLY AS HE KNOWS HE'S GOT NOTHING COMING IN HIS BONUS... AGAIN...
TEE HEE...
THIS IS FUN!

Alex
PEATTIE + TAYLOR
BILL GATES, WARREN BUFFETT AND NOW SIR TOM HUNTER... ALL THESE BILLIONAIRES GIVING AWAY THEIR MONEY... IT'S REMARKABLE, ISN'T IT?
alex@alexcartoon.com

IT'S JUST THE FASHIONABLE THING FOR PLUTOCRATS AT THE MOMENT... "PHILANTHROPY IS THE NEW GREED" IT'S ALL ABOUT RAISING THEIR P.R PROFILE...
THAT'S A PREDICTABLY CYNICAL RESPONSE, ALEX...

SURELY IF THERE'S AN ACKNOWLEDGED TREND FOR CHARITABLE GIVING BY MEGA-RICH INDIVIDUALS, THIRD WORLD COUNTRIES WILL BE ABLE TO REAP THE BENEFITS...
POSSIBLY...
PERHAPS NOW WHEN PEOPLE GET AN E-MAIL CLAIMING TO BE FROM THE EX-FINANCE MINISTER OF NIGERIA WHO WANTS TO GIVE THEM $20 MILLION, THEY MIGHT BELIEVE IT AND HAND OVER THEIR BANK DETAILS...

Alex
PEATTIE + TAYLOR
IS THAT A NEW SUMMER INTERN I SPY?
YES. SHE'S THE DAUGHTER OF SOMEONE ALEX KNOWS... SHE STARTED TODAY...
alex@alexcartoon.com

HILARIOUS... SO ALEX ALLOWED HIMSELF TO BE BROWBEATEN INTO ARRANGING FOR SOME FRIEND'S OFFSPRING TO SPEND TWO WEEKS IN OUR OFFICE DOING SO-CALLED "WORK" EXPERIENCE?
I GUESS SO.
HA!

SO FOR ONCE THE IMMACULATE ORGANISATION AND FORWARD PLANNING THAT ALEX PRIDES HIMSELF ON HAS LET HIM DOWN AND HE'S GOT SADDLED WITH SOME NUISANCE KID...!
WHERE IS ALEX ANYWAY...?

ON TWO WEEKS' ANNUAL LEAVE... STARTING TODAY...
HI, YOU MUST BE CLIVE... ALEX SAID YOU'D SHOW ME THE ROPES...

Alex
PEATTIE + TAYLOR
THIS GLOBAL MARKET CRASH HAS TAKEN EVERYONE BY SURPRISE...
alex@alexcartoon.com

IT SEEMS THAT FEARS OVER SUB-PRIME MORTGAGES HAVE SPREAD FROM THE U.S.A. AND DESTABILISED BANKS AND INSTITUTIONS IN EUROPE AND THE FAR EAST...
YES...

IT'S A REFLECTION OF THE DANGEROUS CONNECTIVITY OF THE MODERN FINANCIAL WORLD. A FEW YEARS AGO SOMETHING LIKE THIS COULD NEVER HAVE HAPPENED...

WHAT, A MARKET CRASH IN AUGUST WHEN EVERYONE'S ON HOLIDAY?
QUITE... I BLAME THE BLACKBERRY...
HEY. E-MAIL FROM OUR BOSS IN TUSCANY SAYING: SELL EVERYTHING.

Alex Live on Stage

Arts Theatre, London WC2

11th October to 8th December 2007

BUSINESS CARD
BIZ CARD

Also available from Masterley Publishing

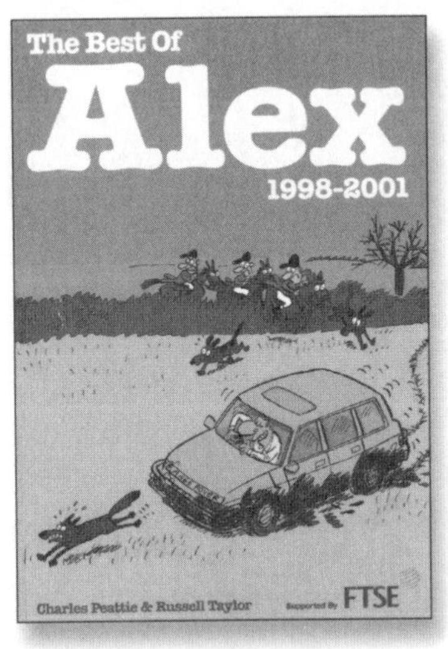

The Best of Alex 1998-2001
Boom to bust via the dotcom bubble.
£9.99 plus p+p

The Best of Alex 2002
Scandals rock the corporate world.
£9.99 plus p+p

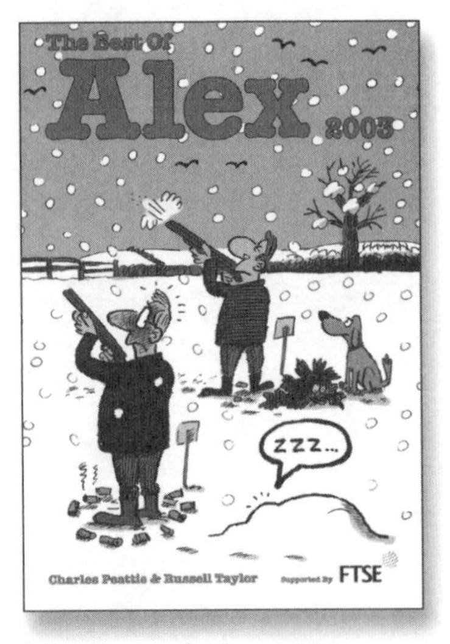

The Best of Alex 2003
Alex gets made redundant.
£9.99 plus p+p

The Best of Alex 2004
And gets his job back.
£9.99 plus p+p

The Best of Alex 2005
Alex has problems with the French.
£9.99 plus p+p

The Best of Alex 2006
Alex gets a new American boss.
£9.99 plus p+p

All Alex books are signed by the creators

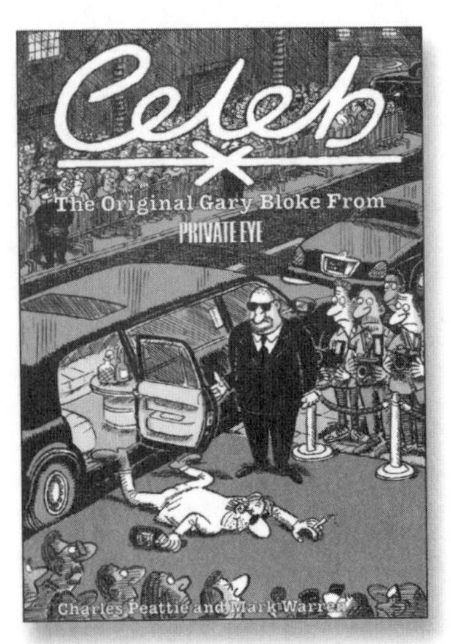

Celeb
Rock'n'roll excess with Gary Bloke.
£9.99 plus p+p

The Masterley Collection
Sophisticated apparel for the discerning gentleman. Share in the ultimate cuff link and tie experience with these elegant Alex cameo-style accessories.
Available from **www.alexcartoon.com**

Cartoon originals and prints
The Alex and Celeb cartoon strip originals are all for sale. A strip measures 4 x 14 inches. If there's a particular one you want, phone or email us some information about it (the date it appeared, what the punch line was etc.) and we'll let you know if we still have it. If the original is not available, or you're too mean to purchase it, we can make a print of it for you. Originals and prints are signed by the creators.

For further details on prices and delivery charges for books, cartoons or merchandise:
Alex, PO Box 39447, London N10 3WA Tel: 020 8374 1225 Fax: 0871 750 2343
Email: alex@alexcartoon.com Web: www.alexcartoon.com